Index

# Index

Bridget Penney

Semina No. 1

*For Paul*

Reading Kropotkin's autobiography, I was struck by his perception of landscape, the movements of the glacial ice that formed it and its correspondence to human history.

The ice is a mirror. You do not see what you want, but what is in your mind. I could see faces in the ice. As I went on, they had bodies and voices. I could hear my friends talking to me, laughing at me. They said—Roland, what are you doing here? When it got really bad I would see people making love in the ice.

# Begin with Erebus and Terror under the ice

'Is Franklin the only man that is lost, that his wife should be so earnest to find him?'
Henry David Thoreau, *Walden*

Under the pole star he watches the polar bears. Strange beasts with their red mouths they seem to him like the landscape moving. Their roaring is the distant clash of ice floes. Though he puts his hands to his ears, the rumble inside his head is the noise of millions of years of ice, and he feels its weight of water under the sky. He falls to the ground. The heat of his body cannot melt the ice. He lies quietly. What else is there to do, alone in this wilderness.

At evening he comes down onto the tundra. The hard ground rings beneath his feet with the clatter of his spurs. He cast his armour off on the ice but it has grown round him again like a snail's shell. He raises his hands. The icicles sprout from them like very fine hairs. His nails are blue and semi-transparent as the windows in a glacier.

*This is an optical illusion*. He no longer trusts his vision since he discovered the speck of interference in his left eye. Mandeville wrote of lands where men's heads grow from their chests and bodies thicken downwards into one enormous foot. Roland dreams in a wood. He takes his penknife to carve a name on a tree. The tree is beech so the name will stretch and grow with time. *Julie*.

A plume of smoke rises in the distance. He sees the tall rounded cone of a tent and an Iroquois seated in the entrance, sewing with a length of gut through sealskin.

*Come inside brother and we'll celebrate the pole star*. The pole star is the bright eye of the great Bear. He doesn't grasp what the Iroquois says but follows him anyway. The tent is warm and full of smoke. He is relieved to be away from the bear's gaze. The Iroquois watches him, warily at first, but when Roland smiles, he smiles too and unstoppers the flask to put it to his lips. The red wine runs down his chin like the blood on the bear's mouth.

ice chips strike lightning
under aurora borealis

Smoke hangs in the air where the bear has put out the fire. As he moves backwards, frightened, his spurs rake long runnels across the ashes. The Iroquois' face is marked with ash. There is blood on his face where the talons of the bear scratched him.

magnetic rocks
violet ice

The bear is afraid of death. He runs out into the night. Underneath the stars he dances, hypnotised by their brilliance.

Roland wakes naked at the foot of a tree. He is hazily aware of birdsong. A scrap of red cloth dangles from the branch above him.

The body, neatly eviscerated, hangs by its feet. Roland puts his arms around it but he can't seem to take hold of it, though the air is not empty. He feels if he could just break through

# Cagliostro: a masque in three movements

A Ceremony in the Temple of Isis, Paris 1786
(following the breath)

*chorus of initiates*

light
steadily
brightening

*maximum illumination*

the company of women are
dazzled. Some raise their hands
to their eyes, the more steadfast
resist the temptation. They are
wearing white shifts, their heads
are uncovered, loose hair. Their
feet are bare. In their hands they
hold stems of lilies, for lotuses.
There is an atmosphere of subdued
excitement. Some have not eaten
for a few days in preparation,
others stepped in off the fashionable
street an hour ago

the girls stir

marble halls, marble pillars
                              wood
painted to approximate marble
richly decorated. Silver and gold
abound

the lovers enter.
SPIRITS disguised
in flesh. Each woman
recognises her lover

what's taking place
he watches without cynicism
as they fuck, the atmosphere
is like a drug, he's aroused but
resists it, he feels
like a god, the hierophant
enrobed in flesh, he is appalled
by the innocence of the spectacle
he has engineered

*the faces of the lovers*
                              wild
eyes unseeing
                              lips
ecstatic,
some fragments of magic

PERSEUS & ANDROMEDA
THESEUS & ARIADNE
ORPHEUS EURYDICE
ISIS OSIRIS
                              breath, he
keeps following the breath

the hierophant
                    naked
stripped of his flesh,
cut into pieces

*return to darkness*

**Masque of the Vowels**

O
ISIS
WE GIVE/PLEDGE
OUR LIVES TO
YOUR TRUTH
OUR BODIES TO YOUR
SERVICE, OUR
OBEDIENCE TO
YOUR COMMANDS
PRESCRIPTIONS

O QUEEN
OF THE NILE
THE UPPER
& LOWER
LANDS, SISTER
& FAITHFUL WIFE
OF OSIRIS
MOTHER OF HORUS
GODDESS OF LOVE,
FERTILITY, GOOD LUCK
THE MOON THAT RULES
CROPS & TIDES, O
LADY HEAR US

*breathe in the incense*

A
SYSTEM OF
MUSICAL NOTATION
FOR THE VOWELS
PITCH

AS A MEASURE OF FEELING
TO HONOUR ISIS

*time is endlessly repeating*

FIXED THOUGHT
ON THE MOMENT
THE TEST

HEART
BEATS

RESIST THEM
SLOWLY

RESIST
DEATH

THE SOUNDS
FOLLOWING THE
BREATH
                THE TONGUE
THE EPIGLOTTIS
                THE TEETH
THE THROAT
OXYGEN
                PASSING OVER
BLOOD VESSELS IN
                THE LUNGS

*vowels alter in pain or pleasure*

from my body
reeds grow.

                    A tree
encloses it
                    Cedar, sweet
coffins it.
                    Linen
fuck on white linen
                    my spirit
fucks the High Priestess
                    fucks Isis
after my death.

## Cagliostro in the Castle of Saint Angelo

where he was imprisoned *having defied the censures and penalties pronounced against heretics, dogmatists, masters and disciples of superstitious magic.* When officers of the invading French revolutionary army demanded his release they were told he was dead. When, where and how he died was not revealed, nor was his body seen.

B             [Scene: a cell]
It is too dark to see
R             anything, but as your
eyes grow accustomed
E             to it, the faint light
from a grating near the
A             floor lets you imagine
the shape of a man,
T             stretched out on an
iron bed, his hands
H             folded behind his head

S             *go on*


young lovely and rich!
            a flock of doves
magician's doves. He thinks of
the turtle doves
            with golden feet
the initiates
            a sound
as of the beating of wings

THE HIEROPHANT steps naked
among the worshippers. At this
moment he is truth, purity. Moving
between the women's bodies,
not touching,
                    the electricity
awe that fills him
fills them

                    THE INQUISITORS
                    in their red robes
                    & hoods
                    (blood streaks
                    shit dried on the walls)


LIKE STREAKS OF BLOOD
SHIT DRIED ON THE WALLS
HOODS COVER THEIR FACES
SHIT PRIESTS,
SHOW YOUR TRUE FACES


*moment of maximum brightness*

                    THE TORCH
FLARES
                    TAR
BURNS
                    RAG
DIPPED

he smells
leaves of coal
he feels he can
hold them in
his hands

*a tape loop runs silently*

he thinks
of the sounds
trapped in
shards of pots
the clay
spinning
on the potter's wheel

'While we were on the Downs Miss Brook call'd so after dinner I went and sat an hour with her. I like her more each time I see her and regret her society more than all the amusements of Bath put together. Among other things she told me she had seen Mademoiselle D'Eon at Dijon and was delighted with her. She says *que c'est bien triste pour un Capitaine de Dragon de se trouver reduite á la Cornette*. I think so too—for with her spirit and understanding what an awkward situation is she reduced to. I have been reading her memoirs and all the letters that passed relative to that shabby business of the Comte de Guerchy and to all that shabby treatment she received from the French Ministers. I don't know whether you have ever met the work but if you have not you will be pleased with it. There is such spirit and elevation of soul in all she writes, so superior to the fawning Courtiers and Secretaries one sees and hears of that she makes all her oppressors sink into nothing. This instance alone I think a strong argument against Charles' favourite doctrine of Male and Female souls...'

Betsy Sheridan to her sister Alicia Le Fanu, Friday 29th April, 1785


**Versailles**

The atmosphere of surveillance is intense and pervasive, carefully engineered by the geography. Wide avenues form empty approaches to the palace. There are glades which appear enclosed and secret spots until you realise another place commands a perfect view of them.

The inadequate education of my companions irks me. They seem barely conscious of the significance of what surrounds them. The forms of the pagan gods that disport themselves among the fountains and upon the lawns are no more strange to them than statues of themselves would be.

At the pool known as Apollo's Bath, water trickles over the rocks. There are ferns, mosses, the white marble group of figures within the cave. Ivy twines round a heifer's flanks, obscuring the legs of the youth who had his hand on her neck. I am reminded of Hermes' theft of the cattle of the sun. Are this youth's feet winged?

I start to strip the ivy away using a penknife I carry always. The stems leave marks like dark veins on Hermes' marble thighs.

I remember the snow in Russia, a voyage across the ice hunting bears from a sleigh. They were close enough for me to see their fur standing up in the wind. Then the red eyes and mouth are laid low by a single crack from a gun. Later I see their teeth mounted in silver round the Empress' neck.

There is fear and delight, fear and delight.

A bowl of salt, a naked flame suggest other mysteries now. When I catch my reflection in the mirror I am transfixed by the continuing struggle between inner and outer forms.


[the hermaphrodite figures
at a masked ball
in Sweden, 1792
ritual slaughter of the king

Tintomara
Chevalier D'Eon]

with holly in both hands
a man's symbol
a woman's symbol

*(prologue: found text*

Last night I dreamed I was the lover of a much older man.

And all the furniture had that light red tint of beech, smooth as satin to touch and cool. There was that sense of opulence about me. I knew it extended further than I could see.

My knowledge was of a different life.

In the dream I became this person, moved with her, laughed in a way which wasn't mine, identified with her speaking to her lover.

The girl smiles. I smile. We stretch out on the couch. He strokes my feet and ankles.

I can feel her fondness for him. He is handsome, distinguished. She does not think of betraying him.

The room surrounds me with its aura of infinite wealth. Through the palace beyond, the corridors stretch away to cool courtyards where giant carp swim under the drops of the fountain which the sun's rays, diffused by the pattern of the buildings and the fine nets stretched overhead, stipple in a hundred muted colours.

The nets catch the birds that fall. Hunters gather them from the roofs with long poles.

The sky above is bright and dark as polished iron. My love's face is a shield.

The woman sighs as he unwraps her feet. I feel her scream rising

then gently exhaled.
I must not let him know how I feel.

Air strikes the exposed skin. The bones of my feet are soft,
splinted together in a compacted mass. They are dead yet
beautiful in a way. I dreamed they could do this to my whole
body.

There are butterflies in the garden, glimpsed through a screen.
The finely carved lacquerwork presents a solid surface but
admits a thousand opportunities for spying.

Snatched glimpses of movement among the leaves. The etching
of white blossom that stands out brightly against the dull sky
overhead.

When she sees the petals fall, her eyes are tired with squinting.
She traces the panels with her finger, letting all she touches
become a part of herself.

A sense of apprehension. Moonlight through the canes on the
golden plateau. She hears the rustle of unforeseen approach.

At night he comes without warning, thin and hard as the blade
of a curved knife.

The hunters with their hidden faces.)

# Experiment

There are two children on the island, a boy and a girl. They are orphans. Both fathers died before they were born, their mothers shortly after. Their names are Roland and Julie. They are in the care of the state, which means, the king. No one else wants them.

The king decides to use them for an experiment. He wants to inquire into the nature of the mind, the origins of instinct and reason, the development of intelligence and speech. He is curious about his subjects, the right given him to rule over them. Are their minds at his command or their bodies only? He hopes to develop his understanding of how their existence touches on his own within the structure of the natural world.

The children are blank sheets, *tabulae rasae*. He orders them to be taken to a rocky island off the west coast of his domain. A dwelling is prepared—little more than a cave tunnelled back into the rock. Gulls pass back and forth. The king watches them from the boat. He has come to satisfy himself that his orders are properly carried out.

The crying of the two babies makes him impatient. He is aware of the noise men make passing about them, the words and laughter on the wind which they too could be conscious of. He stares at the silhouette of the man who is to look after them. Standing in the prow of the boat, hands in his pockets, head turned towards the island, the man is unable to hear or speak. He was born deaf and his vocal cords have been cut by the order of the king. *The children must be totally free from outside influence.* Yet the deaf mute makes the king uneasy. He feels that, lacking the ability to communicate, the man is somehow outwith his control.

In the cave, the eyes of the two children follow the shape of their guardian in the firelight as he moves back and forth, preparing the food for their supper. They react to everything around them. Their guardian watches them unobserved, marvelling at how different they are when unaware of his presence. He sees them looking at the sky and at each other, the pebbles on the shore, scrubby grass and creeping plants and the few utensils in the cave.

*Naming is the act of power: the naming of things gives you power over them.*
The children have their names which we call them.
He frowns at the thought of his own name left behind.

The boy, girl and man on *(preposition)*
the *(definite article)* island *(noun)*
live look play eat and drink.
They run along the paths and swim
in *(preposition again)* the restless sea *(noun phrase)*

'The sea is the edge of the world—the bounding element'

Birds *(noun, plural)*
        fly through the air we breathe—

Gestures of communication

        come here

24

& leave
        (sadness).
Alone, the sense of understanding has reference to things
unseen.


'And then we came to the island. In the sixteen years since I
was last here I have aged more than I thought, for the island
struck me as larger and its colours seem to have leached away.
I remembered the rocks that guarded its approach as inky
stacks but they are as pale and sharp as the stalagmites you see
in limestone caves. I had an impression of futility, as if my life
in the intervening years had been a dream. The sailors noticed
the change in my demeanour. They felt it too. Time had struck
a blow at us, but what could account for it? My hand trembles.
When I try to write this account, reason deserts me.

'We launched a boat from the ship to take us in past the rocks.
Three men accompanied me. It was calm, midsummer noon,
yet despite the sun's rays overhead the chill of the deep water
struck up at me as we glided so close to the waves. We dragged
the prow up the shingle where no other boat had touched in
sixteen years. I was going to leave the boy to guard it, but,
looking in his face, saw a reflection of my own unease.

'The silence of the island preyed on us. It wasn't what we
expected yet we'd all thought to find three skeletons, the man's
and the two young children's, bleaching. What was there to
be afraid of? The only signs of life were the kittiwakes and
guillemots rising from the cliff edge.

'We followed a path worn by sheep. The animals we saw
became nervous at our approach. Here and there we detected
other signs of human occupation. The captain put his hands

to his mouth to call but I stopped him with a look. — You'll startle them, I said.

'Smoke on the wind. We had climbed the hill in the centre of the island. Our ship looked very distant, riding beyond the rocks. There were low thorn bushes leading down to the other shore. The smoke rose from among them. As we approached the crackling of dry scrub underfoot betrayed us. We heard laughter abruptly stifled, and stopped.

'Two heads rose from the thicket. The boy and girl looked at us without fear or shame. In that moment I felt I was no longer myself. I started to address them but the words are nonsense as you see here …'

(We searched the island for a trace of the man but could find none.)

# Forgeries

In summer, ice-cream was sold in the streets and the water-carts went slowly, pulled by horses, to sprinkle the dust. Wild rocket grew by London Bridge and marvellous prodigies were reported; dragons with fiery breath, their wings great membranes, giants at the fair.

The pattern of tattoos had started to cover Roland's back, working down from his left shoulder. Persephone had put them there. She would appear again and work on him as he lay in a state between sleep and waking. He knew better than to protest. She would hurt him no more than she could help.

**Roland Franklin's Cabinet of Curiosities: (26 items as yet uncollected)**

*A book* that contains all knowledge abstracted. I stare at alphabets I don't understand. Their unknown systems thrill me. Hieroglyphs assume the direct transmission of images. I have a sense of power grasped at one remove.

*My Body* that most curious structure: bones, nerves, sinews — the circulation of my blood round a prescribed course, nourishing my skin, hair and nails — drawing in oxygen for my *Brain.*

*The vegetable lamb*, bought from Persia by Mr Tradescant as

27

evidence of the sympathies that exist between vegetable and animal forms.

*A pack of cards* that shows the different phases of the moon. Ascending numbers show the stages of increase. The suits are to be distinguished by curious features of lunar geography (the silent sea, the mountains). The face cards are black, their value to be determined as the player desires. *My knave is Cyrano de Bergerac, who rubbed bone marrow on his body to travel there.* My queen is Persephone.

Persephone deals out the cards at the full moon. Against her dark skin her lips seem dusty and pale. The whites of her *luminous* eyes are tinged with blue. I detect traces of mineral substances on my hands. Often I wake in the night to find my body covered with drops of pearly dew. It is the essence of moonlight distilled by a chemical reaction with my skin. *The mystery I wish to solve is the point at which this change takes place.*

Persephone throws the cards into a bowl of water. At first they float then the water is thick with pasteboard leaves which gradually dissolve. She places a needle on the surface of the water. It spins unsteadily, then settles, pointing north.

*She:* The moon spins round the earth which itself spins on an axis. It is held in place by the tension of the two poles. The earth travels round the sun.

She dips her hands into the water, now the dark colour of her skin. As I watch the ripples her fingers fuse with them. I think of John Dee's black mirror.

*I:*     And the planets?

28

*She*:  The white fury of the morning star, the plangent grace of the evening, are, for you, full of significance. You invest them with the attributes you wish them to have.

*I*:  What is their real state?

*She*:  When you tire of their names you give them new ones. Osiris becomes the Dog Star.

*I*:  Does it make any difference?

*She*:  Only to you.

*I*:  How do the dead know all this?

*She*:  There is no stability in death, no span of consciousness to hold things steady.

*I*:  Don't leave me.

There are individual drops of water on the floor. Rain is blowing in at the window. I look down into the shadows of the courtyard knowing where the ground should be and also that it isn't there. The shadows are treacherous. If I jumped, nothing would meet me. The city displays its true form as a web of particles in constant motion. I could slip right inside it and come out somewhere else.

*fragment of a letter to the magician, April 1779*

... It's irrelevant to talk of love. I think of what you used to
say—that the body was an agent—that you used other people
and they became your agents whether they knew it or not.
I, you said, was one. You smiled as you said that and I thought
how little it mattered whether it was true or not since I couldn't
help but believe it. You had that effect on me. That is what you
rely on in all your dealings with people. It doesn't alter our
relationship that I know this. I know I could never shock you.
I find it increasingly hard to shock myself. If it makes me more
of your dupe, so be it.

What is the point of being in a trap if you're not aware of it?
It occurs to me that people like to feel some kind of constraint
on them. The idea of limitless potential is ultimately confusing.
You at least opened my eyes to what people want to believe.
You never pretended that you weren't affected by the feelings
we all have, or that the insights you possessed couldn't have
been developed by anyone who had as clear an idea as you of
what they were doing. You told me that if your dinner had
disagreed with you or your head wasn't clear when required
to instruct a client you could replicate the effect by a trick.
I assisted you on some of these occasions.

I had the feeling—maybe it's what I wanted—that it was me
who was being tested by the subtleness of the illusions I helped
to produce. Chicanery and fraud, you said, like anything else
can be taken to an ultimate point. If someone was hungry Julie
would you deny them food? If they asked you for a glass of
water would you turn them away? Illusion can be as necessary
to life as food and drink. But it's not real, I'd reply, and you'd
say, what they get from it is real enough for them. You speak as
if fraud was wrong, but nothing is right or wrong intrinsically,

30

only what people make it. Those I practise fraud upon are perfectly willing to accept it as long as they don't have to believe they're being fooled. My crime in their eyes would be if I didn't use everything in my power to maintain the illusion.

Yet some of the times at least the tricks were unnecessary. We'd begin, I playing my part, then at some point I'd realise you didn't need me. When I watched you at those moments it fulfilled some incredible desire in me for truth. That will amuse you. A purely subjective illusion, the mystery approached via the code of a complicated fraud, but still intact.

*Help me Cagliostro.* The city clutters my thoughts with the horror of its noise day and night. These buildings stretching up to block out the sun trap air heavy with dirt and infection which leaves a patina on my skin. *Something is wrong with my senses. They have become fantastic.* When I walk down a crowded street, it's as if I dream it. Those around me take on a familiar look. At first I think they are people I know, then I realise their expressions mirror mine. It seems wherever I turn I see reflected some fragment of my own state of mind.

Last night I was at the theatre. When I try to remember what happened it's as if I'm watching it through a telescope held the wrong way round. I was sitting with a friend. The play was dull and we were more interested in the possiblities of sex. He squeezed my left breast and was about to kiss me when our attention was forcibly drawn to a man making his way past our seats. He was young, dressed in black, moving so carelessly he left several agitated people in his wake. A clergyman who walked like an automaton. He paused before us in the darkness of the pit. His hat and shoulders were outlined against the light from the stage and I had a disconcerting premonition of the eyes I couldn't see. As he looked through us and up I heard the hidden lips say — *Martha*. I turned to follow his gaze upwards and saw her in the box above us, leaning forward with her chin on her hand so the candlelight caught her face. *A vision. I gazed on her through his eyes*. It was a terrible feeling which left me without breath. He had felt rage and pity and love. Now there was nothing left.

I was there when he killed her later that evening. I don't think she even saw him approach her in the square in front of the theatre where he put a pistol to her head. I saw the poor woman fall, heard the second shot he aimed at himself and watched him fall in turn, trying to bludgeon out his brains with the pistol butts until men came to prevent him. People were wailing and continually moving about me but all I could think, in a tired way, was — *it's nearly over* — as if I was still watching the play inside...

# Genius Loci

'The figure of Sir Richard Whittington with his cat
in his arms, was to be seen till the year 1780 over the
archway of the old prison at Newgate, which he built
for criminals.'
Joseph Jacobs, *English Fairy Tales*

Over the hundred years, since the fire, in which the city has
been rebuilt, the streets have reasserted themselves along their
tightly packed curves, and, in spite of the new regulations, the
height of the buildings creeps upwards, swallowing the gardens
and the courtyards of the merchants' houses to lose Pope's
vision of a city of marble among the London bricks gradually
blackening with soot.

One evening in May, unconcerned with their individual fates,
you watch men and women moving back and forwards on the
street below in a soothing rhythm which might lull you gently
asleep if you weren't so bored with the spectacle of the city
turning quietly on itself that you're considering pulling out
a thread which would unravel the whole kit and caboodle.

Unaware of what prompts them to it, the more nervous of those
who pass beneath you squint up at the face they can't quite
make out among the shadows, overwhelmed by the energy that
went into rebuilding this edifice (under the direction of George
Dance, city surveyor) on foundations sunk forty feet to the
debris of the Roman wall.

The late sun catches the façade where classical figures of Liberty, Peace, Security and Plenty pose. Like the original Caryatids, enslaved women, they transmit both a promise and a threat, counterpointing the darkness that exists behind them to bestow a curious sanity upon the government's will—becoming its touchstone, hell.

Your gaze rests upon a tall, long-faced young man, who, pausing to stare up at the prison, is distracted by the figures—so still they are usually beneath your notice—keeping silently to the gate. As it opens to admit a cart, they break ranks and you share his mounting excitement at the sudden confusion in which insults are traded, goods snatched, and blows given and received. It is over as it began, they resume their places, and your spectator lingers, irresolute, before continuing on his way. Your eye follows him to a more fashionable part of town. He is Lord George Gordon, MP for Ludgershall, since last December president of the Protestant Association, and twenty-nine years old.

## 1st November 1793

The instant is fixed on his mind, but when he tries to remember
what came before and after it, a haze descends. He used to think
of it as an external force, another product of the bad air of the
gaol, but now he accepts that it is a part of him. As he tries to
remember why he's here, among the fragments that crowd into
his head there is an ironic voice whose muffled words irritate
him. What he put down in his letters was the truth *any fule
know*. Others had complained about the conditions in prison
before but—apart from Hackman (who had murdered) he
was the only one condemned to experience them for himself.
Though he wept sometimes he regretted neither that nor the
words he'd written about Marie Antoinette—that business
with the necklace had shown her for what she was—a Catholic
whore, a harpy, who destroyed his friend Cagliostro and took
bread out of people's mouths. Strange to say, when he heard
of her death, he could not be glad; though he boasted outwardly
to Rachel, his chief feeling was one of depression.

He has served his sentence but cannot leave until he pays his
fees and because of that he has caught the fever and is dying.
His family prefer that he remain locked up—the government
has bought their co-operation with positions of influence and
in any case his conversion to Judaism appalled them—but
he is faintly disappointed that the new French assembly has
made no effort to free him. As he sees, in his head, the column
of phantasmal and bloody sans-culottes fresh from the
revolutionary wars marching along Newgate Street, he starts
to sing *Ça Ira*, but a fit of shivering takes him and he breaks off,
conscious of a peculiar futility. The footsteps carry on, though
he's sure they're not real. When he looks up, his eye is caught
by a movement in the shadows and he sees the ghost of Roland
Franklin looking at him silently.

No one seemed to know who Franklin was. Gordon supposed it was the way with such people. They came and went at the edges of night in the dark places the city afforded. He was rumoured to be English, American or French. Gordon knew that he had met him once before, briefly, in the Freemasons' Hall on Great Queen Street. He struggled to remember him, eventually forming a picture of a clumsy, withdrawn man about his own age who spoke so little it was hard to guess his original tongue and seemed uncomfortable with the ritualistic surroundings. Gordon had wondered why he was there, but Cagliostro attracted all types, including himself. Now he knew better than to ask.

He would not tell his followers about this second meeting. —How do you do my lord, said Franklin quietly. He rolled a long clay pipe between the fingers of his right hand and as he stood up it snapped and the pieces dropped to the floor. —Will you sit down. Gordon didn't want to, feeling his height gave him an important advantage and fearing the greasy chairs might spoil his new coat. He said —I won't keep you long, Franklin. He meant to sound firm but his voice was pitched irritatingly high. Next to Franklin's chair was a table which supported a book, a decanter, and a full and an empty glass. Franklin picked up the book —The latest trash, and passed it over to Gordon who turned the pages slowly. *My darling love.* —The letters of Hackman and Miss Raye, Lord Sandwich's mistress, Franklin said then filled the empty glass and drank it straight off. The mention of his enemy's name startled Gordon into nervous laughter. He was very aware of Franklin's gaze. *How much did this creature know of him?* —Suppose you tell me, Franklin said slowly—what it is you want from me?

Can you make a revolution from the chaos in a man's mind?
Franklin becomes his brother, the far side of himself. Two
conspirators meet on a dark street. One whispers *Liberty*.
The other answers *Death to Rome*.

## Edinburgh 1779

To Lord George Gordon,

We think you will not have been unaware of the late happenings
in your own country, and venturing from the reports of our
Friends to Expect that our Cause will find in you a sympathetic
Ear, we take this Liberty to address you.

It is to be regretted that Attempts to introduce Constitutional
reform into our country almost led to the triumph of the Scarlet
woman of Rome; By the will of God and prompt action it was
prevented and we think it is some time before the Papists of
Edinburgh and Glasgow will put their heads out from under
the stones where we have driven them. But tho Scotland is now
cleansed We are wakeful until the Danger has been grubbed out
Root & Branch. We fear contamination from the South, & Urge
you, my Lord, to work for the Repeal of the pernicious Act yr
parliament passed last May.

*The Catholic Relief Act, 1778, removed the threat of perpetual
imprisonment from any priest found celebrating Mass and
improved the security of Roman Catholic property holders.
Attempts to pass a similar measure in Scotland the following
year provoked riots of such severity that the Government
backed down. It was the refusal of Parliament to admit
Gordon's petition for the repeal of the Act that sparked the riots
in June 1780.*

'One is sorry that you, descended of an illustrious line of ancestors, should have so dishonoured your family…that you should prefer the mean ambition of being popular among thieves and pickpockets and to stand as the champion of mischief, anarchy and confusion.'
Lord Mansfield's address to Gordon at his trial

'Among those tried and convicted, were several women and boys; but not one individual of the smallest respectability or good fame; negroes, Jews, gypsies, and vagabonds of every description; the very refuse of society.'
*Newgate Calendar*

'Such was the end of this miserable Sedition, from which London was delivered by the magnanimity of the Sovereign himself. Whatever some may maintain, I am satisfied that there was no combination of plan either domestic or foreign; but that the mischief spread by a general contagion of frenzy, augmented by the quantities of fermented liquors, of which the deluded populace possessed themselves in the course of their depredations.'
James Boswell

He stared at the paper in front of him. The ink must be dry by now so why did it still glisten? The light from the lamp had grown low. He would have turned to call Rachel, but couldn't move. He had a fantastic feeling that if he turned his head as far as his shoulder, it would fall off.

He looked down at his hands, adorned by rings with cabalistic signs. Among them was the seal of Solomon. The spontaneous sense of power recurred to him. If he called up an angel or a demon in a circle of flame would it take Franklin's shape?

The Hebrew characters on the paper before him were beautiful. He had written them shakily but there was nothing of him about them. The writing seemed as unformed as a child's. All at once he felt that if he held the paper up the letters would disappear, gliding as drops of black ink over the table. Gradually he was being unmoulded. The haze had taken a solid form, pressing outwards against his heart, lungs, liver and spleen. He tried to call Rachel, but the walls of his throat were so tight he couldn't speak.

He had a sensation of great heat. In that moment he thought of balloons. He had seen one in the sky passing over London. It had seemed to him like the eye of heaven looking down. Now his body was expanding like that canvas sack. He thought of the view the eye must have from above of the city laid out beneath it; fine houses glittering in the sun, the drifts of smoke rising from the streets around the mass of the prison in which he was confined. Although it was dark the eye of heaven could see inside. It could see him there and he was rising to meet it. The walls and roof of the prison could not hold him. Fire and human hands had knocked them down before.

Yet the eye of heaven was afraid of him. It kept him down. It would not let him rise among the stars. He was still looking at the lamp. It had become a black star. The visible world had turned inside out and illuminated him with its darkness. He was thrilled by the divine glitter. How did the blackness come to glitter? If it was part of the nature of things, how did those shapes get here from inside his own head? *They shimmer. Their faces are familiar.* He is intensely happy. How could anyone else feel like he does? But all human faces should be lit up.

Exhibit A

A copy of *BOWLES'S Reduced NEW POCKET PLAN of the CITIES OF LONDON & WESTMINSTER; WITH THE BOROUGH OF SOUTHWARK, exhibiting the New Buildings to the YEAR 1780* on which the movements of the troops during the Gordon Riots have been marked in red ink.

Exhibit B

'I find it recorded in Southey's *Commonplace Book* (BK. IV, p. 371) that on draining the basin in St James Square for the purpose of erecting a statue of King William there, the keys of Newgate were found at the bottom. These keys had been stolen at the fire in 1780 and thrown in here. A quantity of iron chains and fetters were recovered at the same time.'
Arthur Griffiths, *The Chronicles of Newgate*

## 1992

I walk past the site of Newgate Prison, indicated by a small plaque in the wall of Barclays Bank. The space it once occupied is dense with offices. I look right, across the road, to the walls of St Sepulchre's Church, and wonder if the tunnel which connected it with the condemned cells is still in place.

There would have been a wedge of buildings in the middle of the road where the traffic lights stand now. A second tunnel linked the prison with the Old Bailey so prisoners going for trial never got to see the light of day. The floor of this tunnel was thickly covered with herbs to resist the passage of infection. One year, these precautions failed, and an epidemic of gaol fever decimated the officials of the court.

The romance of these tunnels, a neglected, hidden network stretching in every direction under the city, fascinates me.

Close by, a cement mixer starts up and my teeth begin to rattle. I buy a bar of Swiss chocolate at WH Smith and walk along Holborn Viaduct. A bus passes me but I don't want it yet. I pause on the bridge. The chocolate is delicious and I'm eating it much too fast. On my left is the *Mirror* building, behind me, Smithfield. I know this area in my head from reading maps. There has been a building called the Saracen's Head on Snow Hill for five hundred years.

I look down on the street below me which follows the course of the vanished Fleet river. Suddenly I am angry with myself for knowing this, and crumple the silver foil and purple wrapping into a ball to fling into the wind.

*(In memoriam Fritz Leiber, who died a week ago. I could not summon up a smoke ghost as fine as his but have tried to catch a bit of the dark world in the midst of a phantom city.)*

THIS DAY, THE 6TH JUNE 1786, THIS IRON BOX,
CONTAINING SIX HANDKERCHIEFS, WAS
PLACED AMONG THE ROOTS OF AN ORANGE-
TREE BY ME, BALSAMO, COUNT OF CAGLIOSTRO,
TO SERVE IN PERFORMING AN ACT OF MAGIC,
WHICH WILL BE EXECUTED ON THE SAME DAY
SIXTY YEARS HENCE BEFORE LOUIS-PHILIPPE
OF ORLEANS AND HIS FAMILY.

Raise up by Louis XIII on the village's employment of this name, Versailles was at the origine a little castle serving for the meetting of chasing.

From his majorite Louis XIV particulary affectionate it doing fence, which the Palace is the Central Court of Marble.

Mansard been the genius architecte of this illustre Versailles of the only Residence of the world wich the construction's valour is about 500 millions. Le Notre, the creator of those garden, of this beautiful park, of those wall's foliage, of those infinite alley overshadow.

Peopled by marble's world wich the Goddess and the heros seems to raise the guard onder the Roi Soleil's abode.

Fascinate gardens wich sparkling sheaf shooting, the complicate and multiple shoots, sumptuous frame of wonderful feast wich Louis XIV offer very often to the court. Silent grove, agreeable green grass. Complete successfully the palace, evering things are harmony and nobleness.

The interior of the palace subimt with every Kingdom lots modification. The apartments of Louis XV, the fine wainscot skulte are wonderful, light and delightfull decoration, it is all the art of the XVIII cent.

The little apartments regulate to Marie Antoinette are chefs d'oeuvre of the pure and dainty style from that epoch

The palace of Versailles been invade by the people on the nights of 5th and 6th October 1789 and Marie Antoinette's guards saved her with favour and devotedness. it is only on Louis Philippe that the palace received the actual distination, the furnished apartments ussing have been spread about by the revolution, the great apartments been transform of History Museum. The Great Trianon was the resience of Louis XIV and Napoleon.

The furniture been renew by Napoleon. The Little Trianon raise up by Gabriel and offer by Louis XVI to Marie Antoinette was the place of predilection of this queen wich it been enclose by charming park where exalt the Pavillon's music and the Temple of Love elegance and gracefull edifice.

To take one pleasure of diversion she amused herself at the famer wife a miniature hamlet been raise up withe grac and affected wich the disturbance revolutionist surprised her and swept her for ever.

**Emblem:** Isis and Nephthys display bright and dark aspects of the same face. They are sisters, rivals, allies. The moon rides above them, and a cat crouches at their feet. It represents humanity under the influence of the moon.

*The difference between times is in what is seen.*

**One:** A road, leading up to a low white building. A car, driven by a young woman, is about halfway along. Although it is almost in the centre of the picture, the main focus is on a cottage just to its right. It is uneerily perfect. The thatch is fashioned of golden reed and the timber frame reveals the work of a skilled hand. The queen's face appears at an upper window. She frowns slightly, looking into an unseen mirror, utterly self-absorbed.

*(Gloss — Versions of the Antique)*

**Two:** Julie, wearing a white dress with black polka dots, has just got out of the car on the gravel in front of the building. As she turns to lock the door, we see her face for the first time. She has blue eyes and short dark hair. A slim parcel is tucked under her left arm. In the background are the steps of the building, the tops of the barred basement windows.

*(Gloss — Mystery and Desire)*

**Three:** Inside an office within the building. Light enters through a window to the right. A large desk takes up most of the frame. Dr Lavatier, to whom the office belongs, sits behind it with his back to the window. He is middle-aged and in the act of writing, but his head is raised, looking towards Julie as if he has just asked her a question. Julie leans uncomfortably forward in her chair. Her toes digging into the carpet make it look as if

45

she's poised for flight. The parcel lies on the desk between them.
It has been partly unwrapped to reveal a thin black notebook.
On the wall is a row of cast heads, marked with phrenological
divisions. Only the traditional appurtenances of the scientist's
study, the skeleton and the crocodile, are missing.

*(Gloss — Attitudes of Death-in-Life)*

**Four:** Roland watches television in a white-painted room. Julie
and Lavatier observe him through a glass pane in the door. The
television has a twenty-six inch screen, positioned high on the
wall. It shows an aerial shot of a ship marooned in icy wastes.
The camera pans down to take in the upturned faces of men
waiting on the deck. Thinking of an old black and white film —
*The Sea Wolf* with Jack Hawkins and Ida Lupino — Julie bursts
into tears. As she thrusts the notebook at Lavatier, he leans
forward, watching her intently. In a moment he knows she
will turn away without speaking. Her hand hovers awkwardly
in mid-air.

*(The spirit of Andromeda, bound to a rock, one arm extending
to the stars. She is naked, ecstatic. The monster and Perseus no
longer matter to her.)*

**Coda:** *dreaming above water*

A recurring image of an island cliff, sheering up from the
sea. There is a crowd at the top. As they move back, at a
pre-arranged signal, I see the figure in the centre. It is a man
with birds tethered to his arms. They form a mass above his
head and shoulders, a solid, quavering cloud. The noise is
deafening. There are people in little boats waiting below. I am
not sure whether they are to rescue him or make sure that he
does not escape. The sun strikes a haze off the water. Will the

birds be dragged down into the waves, tied to his body, or if the man is rescued, be cut loose by his eager friends?

This Icarus, with his living wings, falls through the air.

# Journal

Night. The stillness of this street, surrounded by busy roads, always amazes me. This experience is common to city dwellers. We shut ourselves off from noise during the day. At night, the silence is almost harsh, its restlessness coming from the sense of interrupted life.

The gates of horn. Waking this morning, I had a muddled recollection of a dream in which there was something about a harpoon. I decided it was the one Sterling Hayden carries in *Terror in a Texas Town.* All I remember is the voice nagging 'Have you got your harpoon?' and the single movement with which the fine silver pike is lifted.

Reading a selected edition of *The Goncourt Journal* I came across a description of a man as having 'a fine old Franklinesque grace'. I add this to my file. The entry before records how in 1764 John Franklin, a ship's steward, was fined 6*s.* 8*d.* at the Old Bailey for his part in rescuing *The North Briton, no. 45* from the bonfire on which it had been ordered to be burnt.

Thomas Bewick thought a rock dull without an inscription. His fixation with marking and mapping encompassed even the human body: he argued for all criminals and others of proven deviance to be visibly tattooed.

I stand in Greenwich Park, facing west, with my back to Vanbrugh's castle in the last of the winter sunshine. Nowhere else in London is there such a sense of the age of trees. In

December, they all look dead. We walk past Queen Elizabeth's oak. Its gently rotting shell is protected by a rail. A family is grouped there in the cold. The children's faces are idle with concentration; they gaze at the tree, somehow I can't imagine why. The observatory is to my left. I would like to find the site of Flamstead's well: I am intrigued by his digging down into the earth to gain a better view of the stars.

In order for a judgement to be accepted, there must be some idea of its being correct. The Reverend James Hackman was hanged for the murder of Martha Raye in May 1779. There were many witnesses to the crime and Hackman made no attempt to deny his guilt. Debate hinged (as Boswell, an acquaintance of Hackman's, records) on the question of whether his possession of two pistols indicated it was always his intention to kill himself after he shot her.

The following year saw the publication of *Love and Madness, A Story Too True. In a series of Letters between Parties, whose Names would perhaps be mentioned, were they less known, or less lamented.* The letters, supposedly those exchanged by Hackman and Raye, were written by Herbert Croft. In Letter 49, 'Hackman' describes the life of Thomas Chatterton, transcribing three poems and eight of the letters he wrote to his family from London. Croft had obtained the manuscripts from Chatterton's mother after the poet's suicide, and in spite of repeated requests, had failed to return them to her. Did this interweaving of the forger's genuine documents with his own forgeries represent a shrewd attempt to enhance the commercial potential of the book, or a bizarre act of self-justification?

We picked up a man on the ice. I hesitate to use the word rescue at this stage. At first we did not think he was alive.

At this time of year there is hardly any day. Dawn comes at eleven o'clock. When you suddenly find you can see your hand before your face in the dimness, you feel like a mole and retreat below deck into the comforting harshness of electric light. There all the senses are fully saturated. The noise of the engine is constant: its grace notes are the laughter of men and over-familiar video soundtracks. The ship is never still, and your body, as a part of it, vibrates with continuous tiny shocks. If the engines are ever switched off, you become aware of the quietness as a numbness in your joints. Once the *Terror*'s ice-cutting gear ceases to drill its way through the floes ahead, inertia sets in. You start to feel uneasy about the steel hull; no longer is it a good strong barrier between you and the sea. The ice moves constantly, drawn by currents far below the surface. It presses in, settles and prepares to crack the steel plates. The rivets are bound to give way under the strain. I imagine the *Terror*'s contents, men and fish, spilling indiscriminately into the water, over the shifting plateaux of ice.

It was when someone spotted him, on one of those wandering bits of ice, that the cutting gear was turned off. A shout came through the tannoy. I was reading an old magazine in my bunk. There was the confused noise of running feet, then that unnerving stillness. I got up. I couldn't very well just lie there. I found myself with the others, looking down from the high side of the *Terror.*

It was foggy, hard to see much, but there were lots of little sounds. I was transfixed by the rhythm of the cables passing above me. A cradle was in the process of being winched up. As the heads of the two men who'd gone down with it came into view, their expressions were grim. The younger one kept looking down nervously at the figure propped between them. He wiped his nose hard on his sleeve. At that moment every detail seemed important. As the figure was lifted out of the cradle, the birds tied to his wrists flapped their wings, their poor heads raised feebly to show eyes with nothing vital in them. Craig, who was standing nearest, cut the strings with the knife he held. The birds fluttered, then fell as dirty white bundles to the deck. Two were clearly dead. The third didn't move when I picked it up but I could feel a very faint pulse.

Lady Jane Franklin, widow, dressed in brilliant colours of pink and green speaks at some time in the future behind a screen pierced with moons and stars. Hope has sustained her but now the searches for her husband have been called off she thinks of herself as an imprint of one of those fossil leaves in coal. The structure of her body remains but whatever animated it has vanished.

I look for the city I inhabit   find it erased
she would exchange
in the ice my memory

The body of the man we rescued from the ice is tattooed with a map of the stars. The thin blue lines of their rays spread over his chest and back. The irregularities of his skin become floating debris in the space around them; a hair follicle the dust of suns and a freckle the flaring gas that propels a comet's flight. Tom added that when they found him he was standing upright on the floe, lashed to a tall thin piece of metal. Once they'd freed him the ice drifted on, a raft with an iron mast until the spring thaw.

He has lost some fingers and toes to frostbite. His hands, lying outside the blanket, are bandaged like great paws. His face is blistered or patched purple where small veins have burst. His hair and beard have been dark but now are white and stiff. The ice on them refuses to melt. (The bird revives. At first I gave it brandy, now milk and minced fish from a spoon several times daily.)

Dear Friend,

I thank you once again for your past assistance in the search for my husband and implore you to reconsider your decision to no longer remit funds to me for this purpose. This letter is very hard for me to write. I know that you, as my old friend, feel you have my best interests at heart. You say that John cannot possibly be alive and that I should go on with my own life.

No one realises how stranded his disappearance has left me. The convention—if it has any bearing on my situation—is for me to wait, like all wives of sailors and soldiers who are away from home. But those who haven't experienced it have no idea how empty waiting is. It requires more than patience. I once had faith that he would come back to me but since this has gradually left me I cannot stand to be so passive. If he is dead, I cannot accept it till I see his corpse. I cannot leave him there unclaimed in those polar wastes. The thought of his body, torn at by wild beasts, I cannot endure. I remember the story of the Egyptian queen who searched the river for fragments of her husband's body and consider that maybe I am under the same miserable spell.

Sometimes I dream of him and he looks as in the moments I first saw him. You were another of the distinguished visitors at the Observatory that day. You were with him on the balcony gazing down on the view of London. Maybe you'll stay here long enough to explore the city some day, you said. He laughed and turned round as I came into the room. I wore amethysts at my throat. He called them violet ice. You didn't understand how I could love him but part of it was that he needed me. If I failed him I could not live with myself. You say time heals but I am lost in *Time's o'er-clouded maze*. The same moments recur to me over and over again.

Sometimes I wake from the dream and hear what passes for silence about me. It is the sound of a car in the street, cats yowling in the garden at the back. I remember the silence of the ice, that desolate country so firm in my imagination. Oblique images fill my mind. I used to feel they were a reflection of his thoughts, a strange hurried flash as if he was thinking of me at that moment and sending me what he could see before him. It is dark and troubled under the night sky but the ice glows with the reflection of the stars. If you have ever seen a moonpath on the sea you will know what I mean. There is a feeling that if you could just follow it it would take you to the end of the world.

yours, etc.

Jane Franklin


The man's screams started early this morning. I was abruptly woken by a sound that went through me like a needle, a thin, uncanny wail that I'd never have thought a human throat could produce. I dressed and went along to the room where he lay. The faces of those I met on the way were uneasy, sickened; I wondered what the expression was on mine.

The captain answered the door when I knocked. He was nervous, out of his depth, but there was no one with more

53

medical knowledge aboard. He asked me to hold the man while he gave him morphine. It must have stuck in his mind that my wife was a nurse, maybe he hoped for some sympathetic benefit. —They're ghouls out there, he kept saying. —*They think he's a Jonah*. The man's skin felt like plastic. As the morphine entered his system, his screams broke down into words. I was struck by the idea that he thought he'd been talking all the time. I could only make out two words, *stars* and *bird*, but maybe that's all I wanted to hear, they were the only things that made sense to me, coming from him. The captain spoke matter-of-factly —The *Terror* will be hemmed in by ice till spring, and I nodded silently, as if it didn't concern us directly, and all the things that were in my mind seemed to grow clearer then. I had the sense of looking through the sides of the ship as if I had suddenly moved outside the time that we were there.

I said I would stay with the man. About half an hour after he'd been given the injection, he started to vomit water. I fetched a basin and supported him over it. Where my hands gripped his shoulders, purple finger marks appeared, mottling the map. His hair was losing its stiff whiteness. It straggled damply across his forehead, and for the first time he struck me as human, no longer this bizarre figure from the ice, but someone like myself, who at some time thought he had reasons for what he did.

The basin held four pints, and he filled it several times. At first the water was pure, sparkling in a way that made me think of the crystalline structure of the ice. Then white traces of morphine appeared and I was aware of a sweet smell that heralded decay. He was thawing out. The warmth of the ship was killing him. I opened the porthole to the grey darkness above the sea. To me, the room already felt like a tomb. He whimpered once, then was quiet.

54

—Tell me, I said —who you are, what you're doing here. You're dying now, this is the only chance. If you have any messages I'll keep them safe. Maybe you have friends back there in the world, someone close to you. I approached him, then moved back. The smell of decay had grown too strong to bear.

He would not have spoken even if he could. I too have that unshakeable confidence that I will return home, I am just anxious about what I will find there. My wife always says I can't talk to her and maybe that is why I go on these long trips. It is easier to love her when I'm away from her. But good intentions never guarantee results. If we hadn't picked this man up off the ice he would not be dying now.

I turned, without hearing anything, and for a moment I thought it was her standing by the bed. In that permanent dusk, she looked tall, and the clothes she wore hardly distinguished her from the shadows. Her face was veiled but I knew from the way she moved that she was not my wife. She didn't look at me. I felt she could at least have looked at me. She bent down by the bed and touched his hand, then she vanished.

JULIE
  watches
    the
       shape
       of the
       wind
       (Samuel
       Bamford)
     a kite
       held by
     twin
     sisters
     with
     red
     coats

to fly a kite
at certain points in the city

is to evoke
clouds

Eleanor Porden
poetess

died
after childbirth

sometimes
he still sees her face
reflected in the ice

56

### The girl as helper in the hero's flight

Julie could not stop thinking of the island. It interfered with the things she saw around her every day so the streets took on a different quality. The bad sixties buildings and the litter were still there, but glimpsed through a luminous haze. The dog and two boys playing on a board placed across a hole in the pavement that she passed on her way to the underground became creatures of romance.

Maybe it irritated her that the island seemed so clichéd. She'd imagined palm trees on a tropical scale, gently waving ferns, associated with the peculiar smell of controlled humidity a great glasshouse always has. A white beach where the spars of a dismembered ship stuck up through the sand. Hidden groves in which the vine rioted and smooth ocelots and leopards lay along the branches of the trees, waiting. Fragments of past occupation—a blue bead, a Sainsbury's bag.

(unsent letter)
…It's true I read philosophers for their atmospheres. I like *Paul and Virginia* as a book of natural philosophy written by a man who spent his life studying the forms of animals and plants. It shows Nature within the human sphere as something to be improved on, and humans struggling with the idea of what it means to behave naturally. (Something you would write off as an impossible task.) The breadfruit tree Paul plants for Virginia is of a piece with the moral tags they inscribe upon the rocks of the island; the state of nature is never a wilderness because each form within it is regular and true to itself…

# Legends

Once upon a time there was a beautiful lady called Martha and she lived in the country with her lord who was in charge of all the ships and men of the great British fleet. Martha's father was a draper and she had been a singer on the London stage when the lord had fallen in love with her & taken her to live in one of his houses where she gave birth to nine children. The old lord who had the character of a rake found the singer made him happy and might have married her had his own wife not still been alive. Martha sang at private performances for his friends in London. It was known that her influence was the way to the lord's ear.

One day she was walking down a country lane when she met an officer of the regiment stationed close by. They got talking underneath the white May blossom. A twig had caught on her shawl and she stood still while he plucked the thorns away. He was serious and ardent, a few years younger than her.

She found she was troubled by his gaze. When men looked at her it was either with guarded desire or some calculation of what her good word could bring them. With Hackman she was purely herself and realised the feeling threatened her. She took his hand to bid him farewell and the answering pressure of his fingers trembled slightly. Avoiding his gaze she noticed his boots like her own were dusty. The white and green of the May tree, the smells and tastes of that moment were so vivid she could hardly stand them. She heard her own voice but not what she said. She closed her eyes so she could not see him walk away.

It changed her sense of what it was to be living. Before it had been the lord and her children every minute, moving within spheres she knew from practice.

A few days later she was with her son Basil on the terrace. He said—Have you ever seen a bear? —Yes, she replied—at a fair when I was your age. Its coat was rough and dirty but it danced. —Why? —Because it was trained to, she said absently moving her hand from his head as she watched the elderly soldier approaching across the grass.

Her heart beat faster as she read Hackman's letter. —Ask him to come tomorrow at four, she said and went back into the house. She caught her reflection in the mirror between unlit candles, her son's eyes behind her, his hands forming the sheet of paper into a bird. (*Years afterwards, Basil Montagu said he still remembered that visit.* —My presence embarrassed him. I was there as a reminder, a safeguard. She wore a yellow dress and poured the tea herself. I played the flute badly and she sang some sweet old-fashioned air. He was gazing at us both together and suddenly the blood flushed up into his cheeks.)

*Dear Mr Hackman*, thank you for your kindness in coming to see us, I hope you will visit again, the earl returns from London next week & will wish to see you. I can hear Basil in the next room, he should be at his lessons but he has a cold and I have not the heart to make him. I dread the others will catch it too, you must excuse me writing of these things but they take up so much of my time. I look out at the sky and wish I could be walking under it. I suppose you pass the days outdoors. When the wind (if there is ever a wind, the air seems so still) blows from the direction of your camp, I fancy I hear muffled shots from your target practice. Aren't you afraid you will set the heath on fire, the gorse is like tinder when there has been no

59

rain for a month. I imagine you have firemen around, with buckets of water and sand, and maybe brooms to beat out the flames. Think of the poor skylark you disturb with your noise. I was always fond of her but would run to startle her unthinkingly and did not realise she sang to protect her young. I am writing nonsense but feel you will not think it so. *Martha Raye*

*Martha*—Far from being angry with you I am angry with myself and yet so confused is my state of mind that I am unsure whether I should not glory in it. My embarrassment yesterday evening must have barred me forever from his house—*I do not think of it as yours for you do not, CANNOT, belong there.* I was aware of his eye on me and on you, and strange to say, it was the feeling of his tolerance that distressed me most. You looked so beautiful, lit from within your skin glowed and your eyes were very dark. That tinge of melancholy became you. Your hands were never still for long. I felt their nervousness and wanted to catch and hold them tightly between my own. When he asked if the food was not to my liking, you stirred a little and I imagined the rustle of silk against your skin. That was why I could not answer him, and he knew. My sense of moral failure was complete but in a way I was glad because it meant I could no longer hide things from myself.

I have written this many times over and burnt each sheet. I feel I have dipped my pen in my heart's blood and cannot believe the words before me seem so neutral. I love you and want to marry you. Come away before it is too late. He has no rights over your soul, he cannot own you. We are all equal in the sight of God and make our own fates. I love you you are my fate. *I believe in you as I have in*

She pushes his letter away and sits very still. There are blotches of colour in her cheeks. Her breath comes very quietly, hardly at all. The light tick of the clock divides the silence. Her gaze settles on the teacup which stands on the table before her. She feels a great hysterical calm, then her eyes open wide in startled comprehension.

## Alfoxden, August 1797

It had been raining ever since they set out in the early morning and Basil, gazing out of the inn window at the dismal street, was wishing that he had never suggested coming into Bridgwater to see the play. He couldn't forget the man he'd glimpsed in the kitchen doorway when the girl brought in their lunch. From the way he dressed he didn't belong to the inn and Basil, his curiosity engaged, had caught his eye, receiving the faintest nod in return, and recognised him as James Walsh, a government spy who'd been pointed out to him in London. Walsh knew who Basil was, and, crucially, all the people he was friends with, and that he wasn't as interesting as Thelwall. William and Dorothy had sat down with their backs to the kitchen door and now Basil wondered if it was because they were aware of the man's presence. But that wasn't going to stop Walsh looking at the three of them, asserting he held them all on an invisible string.

No one came to clear away their plates and Basil wondered, gazing at the congealed food, if the spy had given instructions for them to be left severely alone. Then his friends announced they were going for a walk and Basil watched them become two more of the dark-cloaked, sodden figures tramping along Market Street. He pulled the book out of his pocket and settled by the fire where he found himself reading the same words repeatedly without having any idea what they meant. The fire was smoking with the rain, spitting and steaming in the chimney and the thoughts he was trying to distract himself from were too persistent. But there was no real need to worry about Walsh. All he could do was write down what he saw. At some point his report would be read but for the moment it was one of any number being sent in by government agents right across the country.

He closed the book and returned to the window where drops of water quivered and raced and bled into a general reservoir. He would have liked to open the casement but the wood had swollen shut. It made him think of the last time he went to Hinchingbroke to tell his father he had married Caroline. The rain had been washing all the leaves down off the trees then and everywhere was slippery underfoot. He hadn't expected his father to be pleased about his marriage but the cold anger that greeted his announcement shocked him. He could remember feeling completely ineffectual, opening his mouth to appeal to his father's affection for him then realising it would be pointless. He should have known better than to rely on affection: it was too easy for it to change into something else. His father had simply turned his back on him and from that day they had never spoken. Then Father had died and Caroline too, along with their second child.

He switched his thoughts to the day before when he had alighted from the coach at Holford and taken a wrong turning in the lanes. He had heard the noise of the hounds from a long way off and kept walking towards it because he knew the kennels weren't far from the woods that surrounded the house. The baying was enervating rather than eerie in the noon light. When he got up to the stone archway he realised a man had been watching him approach from the other side. Basil had glanced up at the coat of arms cut into the stone before he spoke, not wanting to seem too urgent. He wasn't sure if it showed a dog with a protruding tongue or a mythological beast and it didn't in the least matter. What counted was the man's sly affirmative grin as he looked Basil up and down and gave directions to Alfoxden, having assessed him as exactly the kind of person he would expect to be going there: another shabby peripatetic who might have just been on trial for his life. It wasn't easy to stop thinking about Thelwall. He had left here to head west, talking of giving up politics altogether and settling on a farm. It was inconceivable to those who knew him but then being tried for treason had an extremely chastening effect.

The size of Alfoxden, once he got clear of the woods, still took him by surprise. It could have held a huge family and all the people that went with it instead of just a young man and woman and a child. He walked through the ruined kitchen garden. Where raised beds had been looked like giant molehills. The brick paths were worn and overgrown but some showed the bright marks of recent fractures. He wondered if his son had been responsible.

He was tired and thirsty but in the enclosed square of the garden there was no escape from the dazzling sun. He found himself staring at the espalier trees which had outgrown their supports. A couple had fallen, breaching the wall, but others still fruited. And there were sprays of redcurrants trailing over broken supports. They shone in the sun but it was not like a reflection, he thought clumsily, more like its light had somehow transferred itself inside them.

His son cannoned into the back of his legs, laughing, and when Basil picked him up the boy wriggled all his limbs like a fish taken out of water, poking Basil with his feet and knees and elbows, then slapped Basil's face from side to side in an experimental way, laughing all the while. There were flushed spots on his cheeks and Basil could feel his ribs under the bright blue cotton shirt. *I would never have dared treat my own father like that.* The boy formed his forefingers and thumbs into circles and pressed them hard against his father's eyes. —Careful, Basil said then —you want to make a Cyclops of me? —What's a Cyclops? —A giant with one eye, Basil replied —who eats boys.

He wasn't sure why he said that. The boy put his arms more tightly round his neck and lay quietly against him so Basil could feel his heart beating. He was surprised by how this made him feel.

At the same time he was caught sight of Dorothy crouching among lettuces where a small patch had been cleared in one of the ruined beds. The pattern of her dress (too small and floral for current fashion) appeared to him very pretty as he glimpsed it through the leaves and his son moved his arms, rousing himself to ask —Have you brought me anything? —In a moment, brave knight.

Her total self-absorption entranced him. He was intensely aware of how much he liked her and the sympathy he felt for the way she struck him, funny and impressive at the same time as she stretched to reach a fresh row or tucked a strand of hair back behind her ear, made it impossible for him to call out to her. If he did she would acknowledge his presence and then she'd just become a picture among the leaves. —What have you brought? Is it soldiers? I wanted soldiers on horses. —Wait and see, Basil said, kissing his son's hair —don't open them out here you'll lose them straightaway, but, as he shifted the boy's weight, Dorothy stood up and stretched in an almost catlike way, arching her back and wriggling her shoulders so he was

64

aware that she was suffering discomfort and he was sexually attracted to her at almost the same moment. But as he turned away in confusion Dorothy spotted him and waved so he had to wait for her to come across the garden.

—Basil. She seemed about to offer him her hand but he couldn't have taken it, holding the boy, so she just smiled instead. He noticed, wishing that he hadn't, that her teeth were rather large and her skin not quite as fresh as he'd expect. —You must be tired after your journey. Come into the house and have something to eat. She bent to pick up the bag he'd abandoned on the path. Filled with embarrassment, he stammered protests which she ignored, only saying calmly when he asked the boy to get down so he could carry it himself. —Don't make him Basil. It isn't heavy anyway.

*The Beggars' Opera* was to be performed in a large hall where a makeshift stage had been erected at one end. It seemed that the red plush curtains and what props there were had got soaked during transportation. Basil was aware of the faint smell of sodden cloth, and in the wavering light of the candles he suddenly wished for bright phosphorescent flares, burning white and blue with consuming intensity.

There were maybe ten people in the audience, a couple of stage-struck young girls with the book open on their knees between them and some lads at the back of the hall who whistled a lot and hooted when the play started. The heavy boots of the highwaymen and the actresses' clackety-heeled slippers set up different rhythms on the stage which Basil found himself following rather than the text. Dorothy sat between him and William, she was, he noticed, holding William's hand.

The two musicians leant against the stage. There was a family resemblance between them—brothers, Basil thought—until the fiddler placed a hand on the oboist's arm and smiled in a way which made him think—she loves him. As she raised the fiddle to her shoulder to begin the tune the light caught the buttons on her coat and they flashed silver.

The oboe came in late and a fraction low, throwing out Polly who missed her breath then gabbled the words to keep up. The music grated on him. He was vexed by the lack of sympathy between them all. They should respond to her voice which wasn't all that bad though she was plainly battling a rotten cold, while she should at least be aware of the rhythms of their playing. She had nice fair hair and plump arms—she did in fact look rather like Lavinia Fenton, who, in creating the part had so entranced the Duke of Bolton that he attended night after night, finally sweeping her away to become his mistress, later his wife.

He gazed at the girl's pink nose. Her powder had slipped. It was poor quality, hardly better than flour, incapable of absorbing the sweat that glistened on her face. He remembered the boxes his mother used to make herself up for the private performances she gave for his father's friends. The powder in them sparkled so that he believed her when she said it came from crushed stones, and visualised diamonds ground up into this silky glittering substance, while she explained to him that there were mountains away in the east where Chinamen dug it up along with the clay that was fashioned into the plates he ate his dinner off. *He knew she had no more idea than he had, and he loved her for that.* He watched her brushing her hair in the mirror and felt it right she should be vain. He asked her once if she was and by way of answer she made him stand behind her and put his hands on her face to feel the incipient lines spreading

66

outwards from her eyes and mouth so he'd know what she'd look like as an old woman.

She always liked to have him around. She would talk to him, chattering away about her own childhood, her brief career on the stage, while he was old enough to notice that in company, even with his father, she never discussed such things, in fact rarely chattered at all, appearing rather distant and reserved so Basil once heard one of the great men quip —*Raye shines from on high*. She was shy, Basil knew, always on edge that her voice would betray the Cockney she sometimes talked with him. The great man had come up to his father once when Basil was with him. —A fine boy. —Yes, his father said, putting his arm round Basil's shoulders from where he sat in the big chair, his swollen legs extended stiffly in front of him —*my natural son*. Basil liked being his father's natural son but was aware the great man found it slightly amusing. —Don't let him upset you. His father's stale comforting whisper surrounded him and the arm tightened. —You're my son. I've given you my name and your mother's a good deal more virtuous than his wife, whatever they say.

That clumsy phrase of his father's struck Basil. He remembered how his father had looked across the room for his mother, had felt his contentment when his eyes fastened upon her, the pleasure he took in her beauty and goodness, wit and tenderness. He felt his mother catch the gaze and respond. She was careful always to smile; she had schooled herself, Basil thought, and felt an agonising loneliness on her behalf.

*My poor mother, she never managed to fit in*. They were standing at the top of a hill under a very blue sky. He was telling her about something, he couldn't remember what, when suddenly she loosed his hand and began to roll, faster and

67

faster down the slope till she was like a whirling top of colour, one of the painted eggs he'd sent down there at Easter. He was terribly afraid, more than he'd ever been in his life, and followed with giant strides, slipping and sliding across the grass and bracken and rabbit holes until he reached the foot of the hill. She was just below him in a patch of lady's bedstraw, lying so still.

At first he did not dare to approach. He was scared she would be dead and he did not know how he could bear it. Then he moved tentatively forward and she was lying there, smiling, looking at him. She wasn't hurt. Her hair had come unpinned, that was all. Her dress was the deep colour of violets. It didn't show any stains. The skin of her arms was faintly tanned, full of health. Her face was so beautiful he couldn't understand why his father had had it covered with a black cloth. He was going to speak to her and then he realised he was dreaming.

The play was ending now in a whirl of music and dancing. He caught the girl musician's sly glance at him, she had undone her coat, revealing a filthy yellow shirt. Next to him, William yawned, and Dorothy clapped with determined grace. The damp stuffiness of the room compounded by the smell of cheap candles had put Basil in a stupor. His head ached and he stood up clumsily, sending two chairs flying, thinking of nothing except how glad he would be to get out into the rain. —We can't take you anywhere Basil, said Dorothy turning to him. —This may not be much to you but it's the closest to Covent Garden we get.

A feeling of sickness took hold of him. He remembered the black cloth and for a moment he was with his mother as she took those few steps out of the theatre and the young man she loved came from behind a pillar and fired a pistol at her head.

68

He should never have let himself think about Lavinia Fenton. Her career was too similar to his mother's, to what it might have been if Hackman hadn't intervened.

*Inverness-shire, 1773.* Lord George Gordon, having been refused command of a ship by Lord Sandwich, resigns his commission in the navy and stands for Parliament. His speaking Gaelic and giving of balls, to which he brings beautiful girls in his yacht, make him so popular that his alarmed opponent, General Fraser, buys him the seat of Ludgershall in Wiltshire to get him out of the way.

*Marie Antoinette* writes to her mother. Despairing of her failure to conceive after eight years of marriage, she does not realise that her husband is unable to fully consummate their marriage due to a minor physical disability. Once he has consented to an operation, she becomes pregnant with a daughter, and, in the years following, two sons.

*London, June 1777.* At the end of a lengthy legal battle over some French state papers in his possession (in the course of which he accused the French ambassador and the Comte de Guerchy of plotting to drug and murder him), the Chevalier D'Eon finds himself at the centre of another court case brought by a surgeon, Hayes, who claims to have evidence that D'Eon is a woman, and insists that the broker, with whom he placed fifteen guineas at the odds of 100—1 in the event of its being proved, should pay up.

*Reflecting on the vagaries* of natural science, Cagliostro stares at the bowl in front of him. Made in England, at Etruria, its black footed shape has a ritual grandeur he appreciates. He has come to believe in metempsychosis, and, if he has a soul, he reckons, smiling, that this artefact should also. The simplicity of its form against the white curtain dazzles him. If he looks at it long enough he will possess it in some way or it may impart to him something of its own inanimate nature.

## Liberty Trees

'The spirit of association and remonstrance is stronger in Scotland, as vegetation is powerful in soil fresh and newly reduced from the forest.'

*Home Office (Scotland) Correspondence*, 4th December, 1792

'It was hung round with garlands of flowers, with emblems of freedom and various inscriptions.'

Dr John Moore's description of a Tree of Liberty at Aire in France, 8th October, 1792

'A Tree of Liberty, bearing the scroll, "Liberty, Equality and no Sinecures" was decorated with apples and lit up with a lantern and candles.'

Dundee, 20th November, 1792

# The International Symposium of Shadows

*Amor ex oculo:* But more by Glances, than by full Gazings

From the bus the other day as it came up to Westferry Circus to leave the island I was sure I saw a horse in the fog. When it broke apart into three men, I was disbelieving. The outline of the horse was still there, more mysterious and potent for my failure to see what it really was.

*Radiating points of the compass — seduction of the map*

He saw himself moving through a city of desire and intent which obeyed the contours of the street guide in his pocket while reaching out endlessly for an image of renewal. He let the bricks fashion themselves and saw the windows lifted into place, pane by pane. She saw images of the buildings in the eyes of the men and women who lived in them. Each impression was unique, converging in a babble which terrified her though she knew that its opposite, silence, signalled the approach of ruin.

the murder of Marat, Paris 1793

'forgive me Dear papa for having disposed of my life without your permission, I have avenged many innocent victims, I have averted many more disasters, one day the people will disabuse themselves and Rejoice to have been delivered from a tyrant, if I sought to persuade you that I was travelling to england it was

because I hoped to preserve my incognito but I have
Recognised the impossibility of this, I hope that you will not
be harrassed in any way at all events I Believe you will find
supporters in Caen, I have engaged gustave doulat to defend
me, such a charge allows no defence. It is for form's sake,
goodbye Dear papa I ask you to forget me or rather Rejoice in
my fate which is in a Fine Cause, I kiss my Sister whom I love
with my whole Heart as I do all my family, don't forget This
line by Corneille

the Crime makes the disgrace And not the scaffold
It is tomorrow at eight a.m. I shall be put to death, today is
the 16th of july'

charlotte corday


place du roi becomes Place de la Révolution

we crossed the Place de la Concorde and walked down the
Heavenly Fields

To make a polar sundial:
take two matchboxes

To make a man:
8 pints of blood
epidermis
marrowbone

To make a revolution:
take hunger, dissatisfaction,
injustice and boredom

foment in private and public places

set to rise

overturn overturn overturn

### 'THE GIFT OF SCIENCE TO LIBERTY'
John Anderson FRS (1726–1796)

'By means of another of his inventions—small paper balloons
varnished with boiled oil and filled with inflammable air—
revolutionary manifestoes were sent across the hostile frontiers
of Germany and Spain.'

*O'er hills and dales, and lines of hostile troops, I float majestic,*
*Bearing the laws of God and Nature to oppressed men,*
*And bidding them with arms their rights maintain.*

**Masaniello his life his myth**

name: (Tom)mas(o)Aniello
occupation: fisherman
place: Naples, over a couple of weeks in July, 1647

After leading a riot prompted by a new tax on fruit during
which the prisons of Naples were opened, the customs houses
burnt down & the property of the nobles sequestered,
Masaniello meets with Count D'Arcos, the Spanish viceroy
of the city, to agree terms.

Now *Generalissimo* of a city where civil liberties have been
widely extended, Masaniello shows 'frightening signs of
instability'—alternately proclaiming himself unfit to rule

74

and ordering executions (estimated two-hundred and fifty within a few days) in a fit of extreme revolutionary cleansing.

Thoroughly alarmed, those who had supported him approach Count D'Arcos with a view to re-introducing the old regime. Masaniello is murdered. He is beheaded with a butcher's cleaver and his body abandoned in a ditch.

The next morning, the weight of a loaf of bread has been shortened and Masaniello's executioners repent their hasty action. They retrieve his corpse from the ditch, sew his head back on, and dressed once more in robes and the gold chain that was his badge of office, Masaniello is paraded through the streets of Naples in defiance of their new/old masters.

*We were happy that week in Paris, at least. Sometimes just before I'm awake I think I'm in our room in the Marais. I remember the honey-coloured walls and the light flowing through the blind with a pattern of the vine outside. I keep on thinking of that secluded courtyard: a woman crossing it carrying a watering can with a white cat at her heels. She began to water the plants on the west side. The cat started to wash, but when the woman moved along, it followed her, and when she glanced up to see how fast the sun was coming round, I'm sure it moved its head in the same way.*

My dear Julie,

I think you are too hard on me and on yourself. You should not allow yourself to be distracted by what you appear to consider 'moral arguments'. Your faith in them I find touching, as your faith in myself. You believed in Reason with a fierceness that

belies your belief, and in myself in a way that contradicts it.
I am grateful that you love me. If I cannot respond in the way
you wish, you must not blame yourself, or me...

STAGE, TOPLIT. A simple rectangle formed by scarlet lines.
The backdrop of the same colour creates an atmosphere both
stark and bloody.

CAGLIOSTRO & JULIE enter. He wears evening dress
under a cape which flicks back as he turns to show its scarlet
lining. He has discarded his wig and his shaven head gleams in
the light. His eyes are concealed behind dark glasses. He claims
the electric brightness hurts him while in fact he is sensitive
about a peculiar astigmatism that makes his pupils appear very
large and dead. JULIE wears a dirndl skirt and patterned tights.
There are scorpions round her ankles, a sphinx at one knee and
griffins along her thighs. The short, dark blue skirt is sewn with
tiny shells that whisper gently as she spins. Her cheekbones
are painted gold in dazzling stripes and there is a beauty patch
at the left side of her mouth. She carries a hinged metal
CORNUCOPIA and a black silk FOULARD.

CAGLIOSTRO binds her eyes with the handkerchief and
leads her to the stool at the left of the stage. She could walk
perfectly unassisted but it is part of the show, the creation of
suspense. He lets her seat herself then walks forward to face the
audience. Their murmur is stilled when he holds up his hand.
She concentrates on the light behind her closed eyelids and
the band of black silk. He is tired and heavy today and she has
cramp in her right calf but they will manage. She is aware of
each nuance of his presence. Sometimes she feels herself to be in
a hive enclosed in walls of warm clear wax with kindred life on
every side. He wants these people. There is a general sigh as his
arm falls, the train of cards rippling between his hands proving

76

once again that only the greatest magician of all time would dare open with such a simple display.

She names card after card. Her hands grow sticky. He has stopped giving her signals, relying on her to float when he rings the bell. The atmosphere is dangerous. She hears her voice, calmly pitched. *The k-king of diamonds. The seven of hearts.* He is using a transformation pack. *Rene d'Anjou. Jeanne d'Arc. Les abeilles alors. Les jeunes filles. La poupée. Le chèvre. Les fossoyeurs. L'armée de la République s'en-va-t-en-guerre.* The nun turns away from the masked bear. The priest hides his face at the confessional and the winged boy advances blindfold with a puppy on a leash.

Be wise and taste. The glass of water is placed in her right hand. When the bell rings she has to name the drink a member of the audience has suggested. She sips. *Cassis. Coffee. Sauterne. Juice of pomegranate. Cognac.* It seems there is a long pause before the bell chimes again. When she puts her lips to the glass there is a faint smell of metal. *Blood.* She stands up and the audience titters. Cagliostro leads them in applause as she turns.

The cornucopia is brought forward. He unhinges it and holds it upside down to demonstrate it is empty. He launches into a rapid and patriotic address, speaking so fast the audience catch one word in three, the right one, Julie thinks, in all languages, all countries. When he holds the horn up again, it pours forth a shower of tricolour cockades. They float up, outwards, over the heads. Eager hands reach up to grab them but the cockades turn into butterflies and elude their grasp. There is a murmur of frustration, growing anger. He's misjudged it, she thinks, suddenly afraid, and breaking her rule, looks into the audience for a friendly face. She seems to recognise one or two, but they

77

refuse to know her. All are pale, and some show the red line at their throats.

She moves centre stage with Cagliostro. They hold hands and bow, but the spectators remain silent. A sharp military drumroll allows them to break position without embarrassment. As the guillotine is wheeled on there is an appreciable stir. Julie and Cagliostro face each other through the gap under the slanting blade. *Only if you want to. I want to.* He shrugs and nods, seeming indifferent, and for a moment her heart stops. She mustn't look up. He waves the assistants aside and helps her into the box beneath the blade. It is shaped like an Egyptian mummy case, in two parts, sectioned at the throat. The mask closes over her face, blinding her. It is plaster, of extraordinary delicacy, as if it could live, breathe and break open where it conceals her lips.

A statue stands outside the gate. Its stone head can be used as a cannonball; its body can crush. Lime trees grow along the avenues. Their branches are stripped to make whips. You see children with handfuls of fresh leaves. They put them up to their faces, then, crushing the scent from them, they scatter them upon the road.

unwritten/unanswered letters

*a Daedalian hive*

Marie Antoinette keeps on her dressing table a glass hive, in which a colony of living bees, fed with sugar water through a funnel, have created their intricate structures of wax.

(Inside the palace, cobwebs turn to dust. There are passages within the walls. Julie walks carefully, afraid a sneeze will betray her presence. She traces the shells of rooms. Often she hears threats and endearments exchanged.

The walls are studded with peepholes. She hears a steady scratching noise close to her head. and putting her eye to one, is face to face with Mademoiselle D'Eon in her cabinet. A pen and paper lie on the desk before her but she bites the signet ring on her left hand, apparently deep in thought.

Julie keeps going. She never meets anyone in the passage, though she frequently sees signs that other people have passed that way. They are voiceless, faceless, cannier than her. If she sensed a living being close to her she would not put out her hand. They are instruments of terror, as she is. The Queen is her co-conspirator.)

—Name and age?
—Julie Dove. 24.
—Place of birth?
—Unknown.
—Parents?
—Unknown.
—Occupation?
—Maidservant.
—What of your connection with Cagliostro?
—He employed me as an assistant.
—Why did the Queen take you from the
asylum for her maid?
—(silence)
—What relationship exists between Cagliostro
and the Queen?
—(secret)


sublime (t)error
—you see, said Marie, holding Julie's face
between her hands, —why it is so important
you should remain hidden.


columb(ine)
'keeping doves was a seigneurial privilege'
no commoner could
after the revolution
maybe slaughtered
doves were offered
in the market square
like chickens

la

<u>correction: idyll</u>
In the boat on the lake, Julie and Marie discuss the concept
of surplus value
there has to be an understanding of equivalency
everything in Nature is inherently absurd

so

—Look, said Marie, —we're not alone after all. Julie followed
the direction of her finger. On the bank, a figure in female
dress appeared to be thrashing the rushes with a stick in great
agitation. —It's D'Eon, practising her swordplay. Not allowed.
She put two fingers in her mouth and whistled piercingly.
To Julie it seemed that ladies-in-waiting rose up from behind
ornamental urns to link hands round D'Eon and, laughing,
draw her away from the water's edge.


*Julie writes*: I find it hard to know what to put down about
the time I spent with Marie Antoinette. Let me record that
she was kind enough in her way. As far as she was concerned,
I was a zany, a crazy fool, and in some obscure way that made
her trust me when she couldn't tolerate those she considered
sane. She became suspicious so quickly. I have seen her fly into
a temper with one of her women and slap her face for some
imagined insult, but she was always calm with me. She brought
my meals to the dovecote where her fancy had lodged me.
She enjoyed intrigue and the sense that I was her secret
ensured me her protection. She showed me the Daedalian
aspect of the palace, the passages between rooms and behind
mirrors that were the source of sibylline whispers and
vanishings through the hours of the night. She washed me
and brushed my hair, dressed me in slightly fantastic clothes.
I think the reversal of roles gave her pleasure. At first I was

truly dazed but the tenderness she showed me made me aware again.

With the first sign of my reason returning, her questions began. I wasn't sure what she wanted to know. At first I was able to fence most of her inquiries without getting too involved. Her impatience made her clumsy. But when she asked me, that afternoon, about the magician, I was caught off guard, and fell silent. She took this as an admission of complicity. As she put her hand beneath my chin to tilt my face up, I blushed, as she thought, in shame, and she said —Tell me what he did with you. We were in a boat on the lake and the light enhanced her restless gaze. —In the temple of Isis, you were there. Tell me what went on. She bit her lip and in that moment I felt sorry for her, her curiosity was so intense. The next minute she bewildered me even more. She shook her head as if trying to clear it and added, half to me, half to herself —I don't think I've ever loved anyone. I took her hands. Without knowing why I did so, I kissed them. She smiled at me then flung her arms round me, embraced me. She was laughing and crying at the same time.

*Marie Antoinette (hesitantly, a delicate flush mantling her cheeks)*: I married very young without any thought of romance. But now I have seen someone I think I like. He is a young man recently arrived in the Swedish ambassador's service who does not speak our language. From the way I caught him looking at me the other day I am sure he did not know I was the queen for when one of his associates told him he blushed and dropped his book on the floor. I wanted to laugh so much I had to hide my face behind my fan.

You are my friend Julie so I need your help. I'm not sure what kind of man he is or whether he deserves my love. My position

82

is highly dangerous, surrounded by enemies as I am. If you would go to him in my place and report back what you think of him, I shall be forever grateful.

> for love
> the court assembles
> for joy
> pleasaunce

The Queen is Marie Antoinette in a red dress seated upon her throne. On her head is a simple garland of wildflowers.


**the interlude of the necklace**

[Scene: interior of a summerhouse near the Petit Trianon. The door is screened by a trellis overgrown with honeysuckle.]

JULIE enters. She is dressed as Marie Antoinette in the previous scene with the addition of a veil that covers her face. She moves with the certainty of disguise. There is a glass lantern let into the centre of the roof, through it pours a green light from the trees overhead. As soon as she halts, she becomes irresolute. The place deeply affects her. She isn't sure whether she feels Marie's gloom or her own. She puts her hand on one of the struts that holds up the roof. The rough grain of the wood, the damp smell, and the beetles she watches on the floor over in the corner make her think of things unfinished and neglected, nature going back to itself.

Roland walks in. Her heart misses a beat when she realises he is masquerading as the young Swede. He looks tired and drawn, older than she remembers, but it is so many years since she saw him and her image of him is incomplete. She does not know any more what to think. Like him she is worn down by the pressure of events that have brought them together.

He puts his hand on her arm, murmuring endearments in Swedish. Beneath the veil tears run down her cheeks. She feels the Queen and she have melted into one, the short dark road to the guillotine awaits them both. If she could see his face it would be incandescent. The temple of Isis was nakedness in silence. In the red dress she feels like Marie, an angel, aware in that moment how deeply she has lied.

### a scene in *Weekend*

I would wander off the road into a field of sheep and a man there would be spouting Saint-Just in some crazy pastoral come to life—the flock of sheep flee towards me as their black-coated shepherd advances, reciting Rousseau

*The world is woman's book; if she reads it ill, it is either her own fault or she is blinded by passion.*

### an incident in the hidden ballroom at Versailles

The room emerges from darkness as a single brazier is lit. The walls are formed of smooth black stones, so highly polished that they mirror the flames. The impression is of a strange, irregularly broken surface. In the middle of the room, Julie is seated with her hands tied behind her back. She wears a white dress which has been pulled down to bare her shoulders. Marie Antoinette, masked and shrouded in black, approaches Julie who watches her quietly with no apparent apprehension. The queen draws a thin piece of iron from her sleeve. She holds one

end to the coals, turning it over until the tip glows dull red.
A tic develops in Julie's right eyelid. She had almost succeeded
in believing the whole thing a charade. Marie Antoinette holds
up the brand. She squints carefully, critically and is about to
press it to Julie's neck.

*With a look I have never seen before.* When Julie screams the
magician will appear and wrestle the queen for the brand. In the
course of their struggle it will slip and injure Julie's breast. That
is the penalty for his intrusion into this more sombre scene. She
would try to loosen her bonds, but she is under the spell of
Marie's face.

Orkney boatmen
eyes of the true seagreen

'It is not easy for any but an eye-witness to form an adequate
idea of the exertions of the Orkney boatmen in the navigation
of this river. The necessity they are under of frequently jumping
into the water, to lift the boats over the rocks, compels them
to remain the whole day in wet clothes, at a season when the
temperature is far below the freezing point. The immense loads
too, which they carry over the portages, is not more a matter of
surprise than the alacrity with which they perform these duties.'
John Franklin, *Thirty Years in the Arctic Regions*


Ice held,

the two ships
*Terebus* and *Error*
float

Ours divided by Hours
the light opposite the Bear


Meanwhile the Admiralty, perplexed as to what should now
be done, were bombarded by suggestions, by rumours, and by
false messages purporting to be from the lost expedition. Some
were found in bottles cast up on the seashore. One was attached
to a small balloon which floated gently to the ground near
Gloucester.

'I can assure you I felt not the least fear of death during the
action, which I attribute to the general confidence of victory
which I saw all around me, but in the prize, when I was in

danger of, and had time to reflect upon the approach of death, either from the rising of the Spaniards upon so small a number as we were composed of, or what latterly appeared inevitable, from the violence of the storm, I was most certainly afraid; and, at one time, when the whole ship made three feet water in ten minutes ... when I saw the fear of immediate death so strongly depicted in the countenance of all about me, I wrapped myself up in a union jack, and lay down on the deck for a short while, quietly awaiting the approach of death.'

From Midshipman John Franklin's account of his experiences during the Battle of Trafalgar and its immediate aftermath published in *The British Trident*, 1806

Bellerophon
Monarca
Dorothea
Trent


EREBUS . TERROR


Enterprise
Renovation
Herald
Plover
Enterprise


Investigator
Resolute
Assistance
Pioneer


Intrepid
Lady Franklin
Sophia
Prince Albert
Fox

Once, as I watched the ice floes turn red with the setting sun,
I had a sense of the life imprisoned within—millions of birds
and insects, and the spores and seeds of plants, which, if the
climate changed, would blossom forth into a paradise.

Remembering tales of past expeditions which described the
plays put on against the backdrop of ice in which the ships were
immured for the winter, I find myself wondering what people
will make of the library we carry, each volume open to the frost,
so stories of love and heroism mingle with science and history.


My dearest love,
                    May it be the will of God
if you are not
                    restored to us earlier
that you should open this letter
                    and that it may
give you comfort
                    in all your trials

                white fur windrose
                muffle hood
                scrape in spite of
                leave smoke
                        lose
                trueheart fish
                        teeth east
                star
                        subsist—


When Franklin stepp'd upon the waste
I gave my love with undue haste
Now he returns to his own land
My heart burns on the icy strand


                        (*after* Eleanor Anne Porden,
                        Franklin's first wife
                                m. 1823
                                d. 1825
                        he married Jane in 1828)

The descent into the Erebus, the Antarctic volcano named for one of the ships in which Sir John Franklin was to make his final voyage, was attempted by a man at the end of a rope, but the attempt was abandoned when he was struck on the shoulder and the knee by two pieces of burning lava and the rope was charred. After this incident, a robot, known as Dante, was constructed to walk down the inside of the volcano. Its progress, monitored from a hut close to the Antarctic site, was to be transmitted via computer link-up to a space research station in America. A few feet down inside the crater, the fibre-optic cable that would transmit what Dante could see to the watchers on the surface was damaged, and all that registered thereafter was static interference.


Ariadne's net
alive at dawn
on the foreshore
dredged up
a tablet inscribed with curses
NEPTUNE it said
MAY HE NEVER REACH SAFE HARBOUR
HE ABANDONED ME

✦

White bride
rises above the lake.
Her smile is joyous.
An elegance of hoar frost
she spins against.

*Signor Lunardi*, she calls,
*let us fly to the moon.*
*The wind will buoy us up*
*and the morning dew*
*drench our faces until we*
*melt away every last drop.*

In Covent Garden, a grove within the city, a dark pastoral takes place. The shepherds, Bion and Moschus, lay the dead woman silently upon a bier, while the others restrain the lover-turned-murderer, to whom the living are no more than noisy shadows.

Owl gentle tongue inspire
turn bees aflame
gold within white bone

### John Montagu, 4th Earl of Sandwich, to Hackman in Newgate on 17th April, 1779

*If the murderer of Miss ____ wishes to live, the man he has most injured will use all his interest to procure his life.*

An awkward, rather cold man, he seems to have veered between doing what he thought was right and felt was expedient. His reputation never recovered from what was generally felt to be his obnoxious conduct in prosecuting his former associate John Wilkes over the alleged obscenity of his *Essay on Woman*. It was his refusal to guarantee Lord George Gordon a captaincy in 1772 that prompted Gordon to resign from the Navy and embark on his political career.

He gazed out at a shadow among the trees. He found himself, quite unexpectedly, in a mood to appreciate the near absence of sound.

## 'The Thorn'

'19th March 1798. Wm and Basil and I walked to the hill-tops, a very cold bleak day. We were met on our return by a severe hailstorm. William wrote some lines describing a stunted thorn.'
Dorothy Wordsworth, *Alfoxden Journal*

And others, I've heard many swear,
Were voices of the dead:
I cannot think, whate'er they say
They had to do with Martha Ray

'Our travellers do not hesitate to treat as beasts under the names of pongos, mandrills and orang-utangs the same creatures that the ancients, under the names of satyrs, fauns and nymphs, made into divinities.'
Jean-Jacques Rousseau, *Discourse on Inequality*

lions and tigers and bears o my

Men used to fear the forests, which were dark and full of wild animals, but gradually they conquered them and made of the trees useful friends.

## Antimasque: in a grove

Marie enters. She is wearing a white tunic and her feet are bare. She carries a spray of wood anemones in her right hand. Her expression is steady. She may be afraid but she does not show it. She looks up at the trees around her. Their tops are so high up they are invisible. She feels that she is looking into a long, dark tunnel: the bit of sky she can see only serves to remind her how far away it is. She brings her gaze down to take in her immediate surroundings. The moss underfoot is flecked with rusty stems. There are no marks to indicate which way she came into the clearing.

She can smell garlic, raw and fresh over the ancient scent of the wood. Celandines cluster at the foot of a tree. Marie smiles when she sees them but her feeling of being watched has intensified. She walks over to the tree and stands quietly listening, then stares at the bark where she can just decipher the long ago carved letters of Julie's name.

**Classification for the growth of trees:**

A lone tree may be a pine or a spreading oak, stretching its branches to create a canopy under which other trees won't grow.

A few trees on a hill make a clump.

More on lower ground may form a copse or spinney.

A wood may encompass groves and clearings but is itself surrounded by traces of habitation and cultivation.

When the traveller enters the forest, he or she leaves the light behind.


circling

(the last redoubt)


my name is Orlando
pure wood wood
mosses & lichens thick
beset grey green stag
beetles they carry

third day we fly to the forest at Fontainebleau trees move with men between them green branches hacked for camouflage cast shadows of the leaves before our faces

'The remains of an Indian hut were found in a deep glen, and close to it was placed a pile of wood, which our companions supposed to cover a deposit of provision. Our Canadian voyagers, induced by an insatiable desire of procuring food, proceeded to removed the upper pieces and examine its contents; when to their surprise, they found the body of a female, clothed in leather, which appeared to have been recently placed there. Her former garments, the materials for making a fire, a fishing line, a hatchet, and a bark dish, were laid beside the corpse. The wood was carefully replaced. A small owl, perched on a tree near the spot, called forth many singular remarks from our companions, as to its being a good or a bad omen.'
John Franklin, *Thirty Years in the Arctic Regions*

her name was violet
no

*branchwyf*

in classical
her leaves
bury me

Julie finds the sun unbearably

In the light of candles she finds nothing, but the rattle of the
bone letters seems too loud as the careless hand rakes through
fingers splayed to form patterns

*whalebone, carved horn, ivory, mother-of-pearl*

She recalls the séance at which she last assisted; the meeting
of the grand lodge in Paris at which Cagliostro was invited
to demonstrate the arts of the Egyptian lodge. He foretold
the future using a magic alphabet and predicted the French
Revolution, the deaths of the King and Queen and the rise
of Napoleon Bonaparte

*or is this hazy recollection wise after the event, desperate to take
control of the flux of history, written as a formulated account,
not one into which you can escape both ways*

left-over shabby images of endeavour
struggling against the natural

—How strange, said Julie—this world is.
(a sheen on metal)

He said, without any form of pleading
—My service to you.
In the Jardin du Luxembourg
chestnuts lie everywhere on the grass. It is not the same at home

Inside the confines of the magic alphabet they felt safe. He was pleased and excited at his role of midwife. They had entered a new life through him.

The French lodge owned the greater power of Egyptian masonry but he could not be triumphant for there is no reason to triumph. —There is no reason for anything other than humility, he said —I am an instrument, a speaking device, as are these letters.

It was difficult to accept that the forms of the letters were arbitrary. They had the power of talismans, mysterious signifiers. They tried to construct a history for each one. Julie looked at the letter A —It's the shape of an animal. An ox. Cagliostro watched her, oddly detached. He never took his perceptions for granted. A continual process of reassessment was necessary. —It signifies the breath, he said—and kingship. He set down the short ebony stick he always carried, momentarily relinquishing the power that his fetishisation of such objects gave him.

# Secret walls

'I mean glass windows, and doors, which let in day-light,
at the same time that they secure us from the injuries of
the air; which procure us in the heart of our houses, the
diversified spectacle of nature, and transform the winds,
the frosts, and the tempests, into a magnificent moving
picture.'
Chevalier de la Condamine


SECRET walls
        2 flowers
hollyhock

                marigold
                (s your flowers are)


                        German lesson,
                        window open wide
                        cold spring kids gather


—ich kann deutsch
. . liebling

Hyperion to Diotima
        —I am afraid
of the sun's bright
carriage, the stillness
of your eyes between
violin notes
        ( . )


✦

scale
face
encrypted
these words
secret walls—
*français*

*les murs secrets*
*encrypt*
je suis à la gare
du Nord
del'Est
these words
beloved—
*deutsch (for sheep; schaf)*
*tractor; tractor (the same in French)*
I am at the station
[          ]
*secret walls*

✦

Diotima à Hyperion
*suis perdue. ton visage*
*enmuré*
*les murs sont cassés!*
*sur le papier*
*au dessus*
*sa tête*

✦

I do not speak German
my life among pine cones

SECRET WALLS
the horses, their
manes black

plumes

(shielded
azur,)
*ma tête est cassée*

✦

Secret walls
immured
            *my heart is black*
blazoned,
on points of azure
            the walls are
stone
or brick
but *shining*
embedded
mortar,
mixed with lime
*a little crushed*
*eggshell*
hair
blood

✦

pont d'argent
            *un chat noir*

*Diotima to Hyperion*
cheri,
mon coeur noirci

in the courtyard, on the paving stones, i saw
letters rise and form
in white chalk, with smoke on the wind
a tale of Hoffman, *un chant un conte*
*my story* as seen
              the veilblackened,
                        torn from my eyes

the trees unblossoming
*secret walls*

✦

Hyperion to Diotima
*liebe?* I am
b-l-v-d,
l-s m-rs
-ncrypt
*-nm-r---*

✦

*my daughter's book with pictures of the weather*
*it snowed. Again. Icy*
*hale. Robintreein*
*gardenchk chk.*
Shift
*my breaking head*

✦

secret walls
black stones
                    exil dur
your heaviness softens me
in the turned earth,
BLUERADIANCE
*doucement doucement*
                    —gently

# Diary of Blindfold

I am rediscovering the immediate. I hold the pen three inches from my eye. Even so, the letters blur away from me. But I'm writing very carefully. I'm rediscovering my writing. Why do I write this way? I'm looking at my fingers and thumb around the pen—like all the pens in the house it seems always on the verge of running out of ink. Normally I never examine my fingers so close up. The skin is very rough and cracked. Round the nails, especially. I can see the lines of dirt under my nails that I always mean to do something about. My hands seem permanently dirty. I don't know why.

What do you mean by not being able to see? I'm trying to think about it. Two mornings ago, there was freezing fog which did not lift all day, and when I got up early to go to work, the pavement was black, sheer and glistening—at least I pictured it so when I tried to walk and found my feet slipping, for if I could see my hand in front of my face that was all. While I waited for the bus I was more jumpy than usual, as I could not see what was coming, and the park on the far side of the road was invisible—the fog so thick I could not even discern the absence of buildings.

It's strange how the sentence escapes me. Because I can't keep it all under my eyes, I have to remember it in my head. I find that difficult. What does this say about me? That I'm not used to it. It's too easy to rely on the eye. Everything I'm used to in the world is visual. This text has a serial integrity. I cannot read what I've written, I form it as I go along.

This is a notebook of lost and founds. I can write without seeing what I write. You have no idea how liberating this appears to me.

Her name is Flora. If she was in the street and a military band went past, she had to stop her hand from rising in salute.

It is Christmas Eve. Children are whooping in the street outside. It is six days since the end of the diary of blindfold.

## Grandmother/Grandfather

Why am I thinking about Flora? Because I read about her somewhere and she comes to mind like a character in a story I've already written.

I can't imagine what it must have been like to fight in the First World War. When I was growing up there was more of a link with that time.

Both my grandmothers were born in 1898. They were sixteen when the war began, twenty when it ended. Their lives were very different, but had this common shaping factor. My mother too grew up during a war. She was eighteen in 1945, my father four years younger.

I've heard it said that people who have fought together always know each other. That war puts a stamp on people, marking them out for the rest of their lives.

My grandfather lost an eye and a lung in the war to shrapnel and mustard gas. In their wedding photo he stands beside my grandmother. It seems they are both leaning slightly towards the camera. She wears a long veil with a circlet of flowers round her head. I can't remember her expression. He wears an eye patch. The effect is not rakish, but grim. He died in his forties, a long term casualty. My grandmother remained a widow for thirty years.

I helped clear out her house after she died. I was maybe fourteen at the time. The house was tall and chilly. It was the place where she had spent all her married life and widowhood. When we'd stayed there, many Christmasses before, my sister and I slept in the room our father had once occupied. It still had children's books in it, some toys. Now, sorting through the accumulated litter of her possessions, came a fresh sense of surprise. At fourteen I'd started to become curious in a new way. I was mostly self-absorbed, but to things I could read as a part of my own history I was intensely open.

What was it like to marry a man who came back from the war? Could she have let herself think about what might have been. Behind my grandmother's neat water-colours there was no sense of personality at all.

## Flora

—My father, she sighed. —I loved my father. I did everything I could to please him.

Her father was a self-educated man. He developed an addiction to learning, passed on to her everything he knew. To teach her helped him to get things clear in his own mind. He was ex-army, walked with a limp. She liked the way he walked. It never struck her that there was anything wrong.

Flora is in an old folk's home. She will be eighty next month. She wouldn't mind the place so much, she's been in hospital, worse places, but here the television is on quite loud all day and she cannot get used to it. When she tells the nurse who is combing her hair that she never had television before the nurse looks at her, thinking she's senile.

—What did you do all day?
—I had plenty to do, Flora said clearly, thinking back to the days before she broke her hip and ended up here. The nurse passes her a mirror. She studied her reflection, thinking—who is this old woman? and says to the nurse (who's young, her favourite)—how do you stand being around old people all day? The nurse smiles at her. —It's my job. She turns away to lay down the mirror and comb, then says abruptly
—So what did you do when you were my age?
—I was in the army, Flora said.
—What did you do? the nurse repeated, taking the crimson scarf higher round Flora's neck.
—I was a soldier.

It was a long time since she'd said it to anyone, not forgetting but trying to live it down, integrating unsuccessfully with the life she was expected to lead. She felt herself stiffen a little, pride maybe, ridiculous in any case. She wanted to laugh at herself and was glad that her tear ducts were so old and useless there was no danger of her weeping.

—I'm not senile.
She met the girl's uneasy gaze. —I was a transvestite.

The effect of the word was so clearly shocking on the young woman's face. Old people weren't supposed to know such words. Age made them innocent. The world had been more innocent when they were young.

—You fought? said the nurse—You killed people then.
Flora sighed. —They were the enemy. It was war. You can't understand. I can't justify myself to you now.

Among my grandmother's possessions was a box with a decorated lid. On it was a picture of a lady in a ball-gown by a window. As I held it up to the light, it glittered and shimmered, turning from blue to green. The skirt was fashioned from a butterfly's wing. When I realised that I never touched it again.

✦

Other things happen in the diary of blindfold. Everyday things have become fiddly, making a cup of tea is a complicated process when I can hardly see. Worried that I'll hurt myself at first, Paul insists on doing everything for me—it's rather nice to be waited on hand and foot but after a few hours it's just frustrating—and I sneak away when he's busy or asleep. I find I can do most things as long as I'm careful, it's just the margin of error is so small and the detail of objects when I peer at them close up becomes distracting.

We walked over to Whitechapel. It was raining very lightly when we left, and he'd rather have taken the tube but I said that I wanted to be in the fresh air and the underground would confuse me, I'd find the darkness in the tunnels and the bright lights too disorienting. Besides it will stop raining darling (it didn't). He held an umbrella over us both and I couldn't see myself getting wet, it became apparent only as my clothes started to feel damp. We walked across the common, traversed the bridge over the canal, along back streets, past workshop units, Paul telling me when to mind the pavement and cross the road. Bored, fed-up, and even more ungracious than usual, I was perversely determined to prove (though I was glad he was there) that I could manage on my own—I saw that kerb, yes, and I know the pavement dips there because I've walked this way so many times, there's the railing, yes, and we have reached the road. Cars approach, their lights blur, spangle and fracture, growing huge. That sounds like a lorry which way is it coming? I realise I can't separate out noises directionally at all. Is this something that people who are not just blindfold but really blind learn to do?

We're walking past the Trinity almshouses which echo the sea in every curve of their construction: rigged ships perched at each corner, monsters' faces and the delicate openings of shells over doorways and windows. The roof beams are old ships' timbers.

Buildings appear skeletal. They're hard to describe. Lines and angles dominate. The people walking towards me are sticks on two legs with round heads. The face of the blind have a different set of expressions. I wonder what my own face looks like.

*1915* —Flora paused in front of the photographer's shop in the main street of a small town miles from anywhere except the military training camp. Her hands shook as she lit a cigarette. She was suffering from a serious failure of nerve as she stared at her uniformed reflection among the framed prints in the window—the weddings, babies, and the pictures of young girls to give to their friends. She had never felt she fitted in before, but now she was sick at heart with the hundred small embarrassments and uncertainties arising from her changed state.

Tired of looking, she was about to move on when she heard a girl's voice calling her—hey soldier soldier boy where are you off to in such a hurry?

The interior of the shop was dark, crowded with equipment and smelt of chemicals. —I'm Maud, said the girl —my father's away today, he's photographing a wedding over at _____. Flora smiled though the name meant nothing to her, looking around as her eyes became used to the gloom. —I was watching you from the window, said Maud —there's nothing much else to do here. You're from London, aren't you. What's your name? —Gerrard, Flora said. She was suddenly nervous of Maud. There was an intensity in her eyes, the face framed by dark ropes of hair. —Do you want your picture done, Mister Gerrard?

Maud smiled then, seeming self-conscious, and turned away, picking a stray black hair off the pink knitted cardigan she wore. —I'll do it for free as my contribution to the war effort. From your face you must be a good fighter, Gerrard.

Flora laughed then. Maud brought out her own recklessness, and she was aware of a freedom in her position that was unfamiliar, elating. Maud unlocked a door at the back of the shop. As Flora stepped through, she glanced up. Several heavy wooden rollers were suspended from the ceiling. —These are the backdrops, Maud said quietly, almost uneasy. —I think we should use this one for you.

What had she expected when Maud pulled the cord and the canvas unrolled too quickly, raising all the dust? Not this, not the crowded intensity of colour, abstract shapes settling into a foreign landscape, a village in the background but not like here, smooth rolling hills, a meadow crammed with flowers. In the foreground was a tree with spreading branches and fruit growing among the leaves. —You painted this? Flora said turning. Maud nodded. All at once she seemed older, weary, and when she smiled Flora felt she knew how she'd look when she was an old woman.

It was scary and very strange. It made her think would she even be alive a year from today. Would the war be over? What else would have happened?

During the First World War phosphorescent paint was applied to the grass in London parks with the idea of fooling enemy planes into believing they were large buildings lit up.

**the iconography of the female warrior**

On medals, Renaissance princes had themselves depicted as armed women, reconciling Mars and Venus. Queen Christina, Garbo's uncomfortable laugh. Kleist's Penthesilea, Amazon turned vampire feeding on her lover's flesh. Phoebe Hessel, who served in the English army during the eighteenth century and is buried in Brighton where she died aged one hundred and eight.

Flora had one particular friend while she was in the army. His name was Leonard. He spent all his time reading, he would read anything, old newspapers, manuals, that he could get his hands on.

They talked about London. They talked about Victoria Park. She tried to imagine it with the grass painted silver. It would shine like a great unearthly lake, in the moonlight glowing, the trees would rise up out of the lake. The flamingoes which lived on the pond would walk across the phosphorescent grass.

**ghost of Maud the painter**

In Flora's imagination she always appears as on the day of the
photograph. Ghosts should be dressed in white but Maud is
resolutely technicolour.

—Why did you cut your throat?
Maud points to her neck. She tries to speak but there is only
an ugly gasping sound.
Flora wakes shivering.

when reading becomes difficult
you start to think about it

when walking is difficult
when speech is hard for some reason

the primacy of the visual sense
if we could see ghosts walking in daylight
Chinese ghosts with black spittle

paper motorcycle   typewriter
paper Walkman
shoes made beautifully of paper
Hell passport, bank notes
entering  another country with due precaution

Hell's windows
play ball
bouncing
a soft paper ball
that makes no sound
won't fly straight

Tiresias could speak without blood
'the sense of the pleasure she gave
doubled her own pleasure'

in cold hell
Blindfold's *Black Book*

'and then Ille'

when this you see remember me
when/this/you/see/remember/me
remember me but oh forget my fate

**amour**

Maud:  keeper of the gate
Maud Ruthyn

serpent coils
girls in white dresses
(some of Maud's paintings have the qualities
of pornography the cold eye)
hard
Maud sits in a room, reading
she has one eye on the camera taking the picture

her own camera
she is frozen there by her own
resolution

Amour: his eyes are blindfolded with a black cloth.
He is naked, flambeaux in his crossed hands

She kisses him on the knee
she feels the movement
of the plates of bone
under fluid
she presses her tongue against his kneecap
sliding her hands
up the back
of his thighs
she tastes the skin of his thigh
slightly salt
she lets her tongue find him
how to awaken him
he's like a statue
she takes his dick in her mouth

she sucks
she pushes
the skin back
gently
with the very edges of her teeth
she thinks of things for her tongue to do
it seems
too big
for her mouth
she pushes
teases it around
her hands clasp his buttocks

the torches above her head tremble
she feels
the muscles tense
in his back
she hears his voice
he is no longer silent
he cries out
marvellous words of love

*Tuesday, 28th January:* a disappointment. I walked over to the Whitechapel Gallery curious to view the exhibition *A cabinet of signs* I'd visited seven weeks before with seriously restricted vision. I avoided the dioramas with wildebeest my eyes had previously inched over. I looked at the books made of cut-up comics (X-Men and bathing belles), sleek machines showing a raw image of human flesh, white pillars with cool messages, flashing lights revealing numbers where there had been a blur. It was the last free day so the gallery was quite crowded. Lots of people were drawing things. Why is the sight of people drawing in an art gallery so bizarre.

Alison is going to Japan in two months' time. She is to sublet her brother's flat in Tokyo and teach English to Japanese kids. She expects to find it much easier than what she's doing now. I said—you've got to be joking, teaching kids? but she says they've all been learning English for six years already and can read and write it's just the speaking they're not confident about. I told this to Mark and he said that's right, teaching English in Japan you do it totally on your own terms and don't have to know any Japanese. I like the thought of Alison speaking English to all these Japanese kids. She has a few contacts over there, she's really looking forward to it, even the gardens, she says, are like works of art.

I remember a postcard my uncle sent me from Tokyo. It showed the hotel garden. He said he'd tried to find it and when he did he discovered the space was so small you couldn't really go in it, you just looked at the arrangement of rocks, the fountain falling into a stream and carefully tended plants. I made a miniature garden in a pie dish. The ground was moss I scraped off a stone. It was brighter than grass and somehow exciting even in the ragged patchwork I made of it. There was a pond in the middle, silver foil or a fragment of mirror. I edged it with tiny white stones I picked up from the gravel, but was dissatisfied. I wanted an effect like flowers or stars. The stones would never unfold like wood anemones. The pond was in stasis. It could not ripple. When I stared down into it, it returned an unwinking reflection of my own eye.

## flowers are for

The fields are full of flowers. The fields are full of women.
Crimson poppies, brave women. The army is made up of
women soldiers massed against the sky and mud. —What
would it, Flora thought—what would it be like?

She leans against a tree. Once the landscape was green. All
the leaves have gone now. The trunk was blackened by the
explosion that blew them away. Ash has scored deeply into its
bark. What does the landscape betray? It is covered by a fine
grey cloud that sometimes rises and fills the air. It gets in your
eyes and furs your tongue, but it's not like gas. You can close
your eyes against the cloud. With its poison, the gas turns your
whole body inside out.

She shifts position and presses her face against the trunk. The
stark outline of the tree offers limited protection. Her clothes
are wet through and the strap of her rifle digs into her shoulder.
It isn't loaded. She would not have time to fix the bayonet in
place if she was attacked.

It is so quiet. There are men back there behind the mounds of
earth she helped to dig, packed icy hard now and slippery as
glass with the morning's frost. They are talking and smoking,
singing, playing cards. The boredom they all have to face is
the unutterable thing. Waiting for something you know will
happen makes you want it to happen however much you
are afraid.

She can only imagine this land in its outline. Where have the
birds gone? She is the only living thing. The soldiers march
and turn everything to mud under the sky.

At moments like this it's better not to think. She is part of the mood that grips them all. She has to do well, there is that in her, but it is fear that drives her, a strange notion of dying unfulfilled.

**Maud the painter**

Maud the painter  Maud my sister  Maud the impatient

She is reading *Uncle Silas*. She likes books in which she appears.
She flips from page to page, drawing pictures in the margin.
Her sketches start to enclose the words. She circles words that
take her fancy, drawing them out of their place in a sentence
to let them stand forth as raw material. MAUD. She isolates
her name. HAGGARD. PALLID. TRANCE. I WAS
MORE NERVOUS AND MORE IMPETUOUS,
AND MY FEELINGS BOTH STIMULATED AND
OVERPOWERED ME MORE EASILY. PROFANED.
TRANSFIXED. HE GOES BY THE EYE AND BY
SENSATION. HAUNTED REGIONS. THE SERPENT
BEGUILED HER AND SHE DID EAT.

Maud finds herself staring into the mirror above the fireplace.
The reflection is dim but then her eyes clear and she sees her
lover standing by the French window. He is tall and dark,
no longer blindfolded. When he smiles at her his eyes are
piercing rays.

—What do you want? Maud says. Though barely into middle
age her face is lined and her hair already white. —You left me,
remember. I thought you'd done with me a long time ago.

He is changing as she speaks. When he opens his mouth
millions of sparks waver on the air. —Maud, he says—Love
is eternal wherever you take it.

She feels the heat of his breath, no, it's the heat of the fire in the
grate. She takes in the familiar objects around her, the clock
with its subdued tick, the calendar on the wall which says 1934.

She opens the window out into the yard. It has been raining. The smell of the wet city night enters the room. It's full of smoke and stars. She can hear voices in the next street. She feels remote from them. She looks at her pictures propped around the room. A detail catches her eye here and there: an arm, a throat, a branch, the eyes of death looking at her through the leaves.

✦

In one sketch there is nothing but ribbons. Ribbons are for a bride. When she walks and talks. When she kneels and stands and sits. Ribbons are to cover her. They are one colour, all colours of blue. They change according to her mood. Some are deep indigo. She lies.

Sections (or earlier versions thereof) of *Index* appeared in the magazines *Bakunin*, *Chapman*, *Hanging Loose* and *West Coast Line* and in the anthologies *A Curious Architecture* (Stride, 1996) and *Suspect Device* (Serpent's Tail, 1998). I am grateful to all concerned. I wish to record my debt to the people whose words I have wrenched from their original context to make part of my book. Thank you, especially to those I have not acknowledged, often through not knowing their names. Kingsland Waste Market was, on two widely separated occasions, the source of material which helped give this book its form, and so, to whatever its presiding genius may be, my salutations. Thanks are also due to Fraser Muggeridge for his design work and everyone at Book Works; especially Stewart Home for commissioning *Index* and Gavin Everall for all his careful work on a confusing manuscript and very many helpful suggestions.

*Index*
Bridget Penney
Semina No. 1
Published and distributed by Book Works, London
First edition, 2008
Second edition, 2015

ISBN 978 1 906012 03 8

Commissioning editor: Stewart Home
Edited by Stewart Home and Gavin Everall
Designed by Fraser Muggeridge studio
Printed by Intype Libra

Book Works
19 Holywell Row
London
EC2A 4JB
www.bookworks.org.uk
tel: +44 (0)20 7247 2203

Book Works is funded by Arts Council England